Horizons
Phonics & Reading
1

Student Book One

Author:

Polly A. Wood, M.A.

Editor:

Alan Christopherson, M.S.

Graphic Design:

Jennifer Davis

Illustration:

Alpha Omega Creative Services

Alpha Omega Publications • Chandler, Arizona

Printed in the United States of America

ISBN 0-7403-0317-1

Lesson 1

Beginning Consonant/Vowel Sounds

Name: _____

1. Say the name of each picture. Print the capital and lower case *consonant* letters for its *beginning* sound.

2 Say the name of each picture. Print the capital and lower case *vowel* letters for its *beginning* sound.

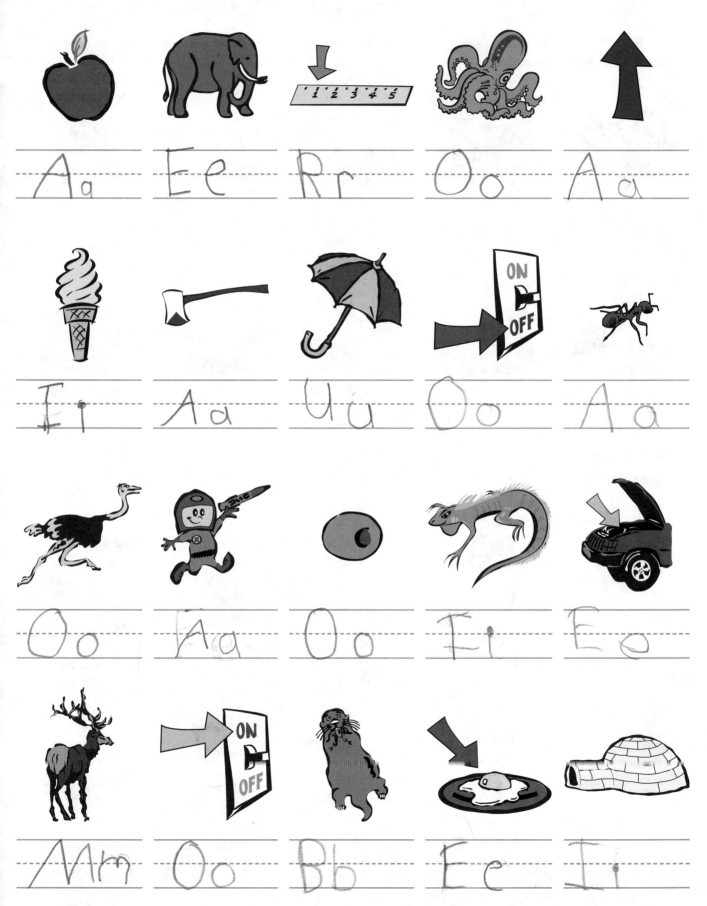

Aa   Ee   Rr   Oo   Aa

Ii   Aa   Uu   Oo   Aa

Oo   Aa   Oo   Ii   Ee

Mm   Oo   Bb   Ee   Ii

Horizons® Phonics & Reading Grade 1 Student Book One

3 Say the name of each picture. Finish the words under each picture with the short vowel sound.

b e d   g u m   h o t   b a t   p i g

4 Practice reading these beginning blends. Use the short vowel sound.

b + a = ba	d + a = da	n + a = na
b + o = bo	d + o = do	n + o = no
a + b = ab	a + d = ad	a + n = an
o + b = ob	o + d = od	o + n = on

5 Add the ending sounds.

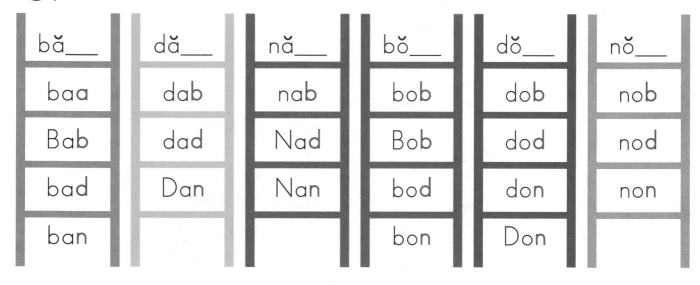

bă___	dă___	nă___	bŏ___	dŏ___	nŏ___
baa	dab	nab	bob	dob	nob
Bab	dad	Nad	Bob	dod	nod
bad	Dan	Nan	bod	don	non
ban			bon	Don	

6 Practice reading these ending blends. Use the short vowel sound.

a + b = ab	a + d = ad	a + n = an
o + b = ob	o + d = od	o + n = on

7 Add the beginning sounds.

___ăb	___ăd	___ăn	___ŏb	___ŏd	___ŏn
Bab	ad	an	bob	odd	on
dab	add	ban	Bob	bod	bon
nab	bad	Dan	dob	dod	don
	dad	Nan	nob	nod	Don
	Nad				non

Middle Consonant
Sounds

Name:

◆ Say the name of each picture. Write the capital and lowercase letters for its *middle* consonant sound.

T t   P p   B b   M m

D d   V v   G g   M m

X x   G g   B b   P p

N n   L l   T t   L l

Practice reading these beginning blends. Use the short vowel sound.

f + a = fa	f + o = fo	f + e = fe	f + i = fi
h + a = ha	h + o = ho	h + e = he	h + i = hi
t + a = ta	t + o = to	t + e = te	t + i = ti

3 Add the ending sounds.

fă___	fŏ___	fĕ___	fĭ___	hă___	hŏ___
fab	fob	fed	fib	had	hob
fad			fin	hat	hot
fan			fit		
fat					

hĕ___	hĭ___	tă___	tŏ___	tĕ___	tĭ___
hen	hid	tab	Todd	Ted	tiff
	hit	tad	tot	ten	tin
		Tad			
		tan			

Practice reading these ending blends. Use the short vowel sound.

a + b = ab	e + b = eb	i + b = ib	o + f = of
a + h = ab	e + d = ed	i + d = id	o + d = od
a + t = at	e + t = et	i + t = it	o + t = ot

5 **Add the beginning sounds.**

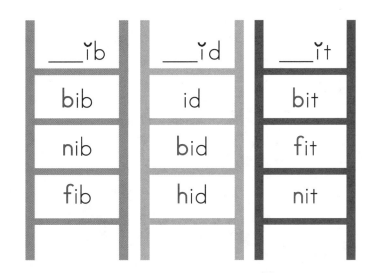

___ăb	___ăt	___ŏd	___ŏt	___ĕd	___ĕt
nab	at	odd	dot	Ed	bet
tab	bat	nod	hot	bed	net
	hat	Todd	not	fed	
	Nat		tot	Ned	

___ĭb	___ĭd	___ĭt
bib	id	bit
nib	bid	fit
fib	hid	nit

Draw a line to match the words that rhyme.

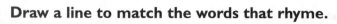

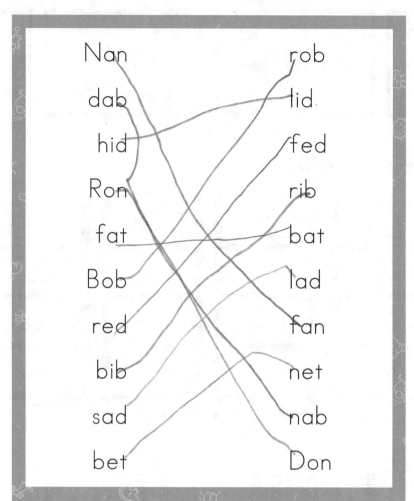

Nan	rob
dab	lid
hid	fed
Ron	rib
fat	bat
Bob	lad
red	fan
bib	net
sad	nab
bet	Don

Lesson 3

Ending Consonant
Sounds

Name: _____

1 Say the name of each picture. Write the lower case letter for its *ending* sound.

Tt　　Pp　　Nn　　Rr　　Ll

Dd　　Ff　　Tt　　Xx　　Ss

Pp　　Tt　　Gg　　Ss　　Pp

2 Now think of some words that end in *x*, *p*, *k*, or *m*.

3 Review the beginning letter sounds. Write the *beginning* lower case letter for each picture.

   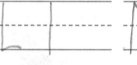 

U u   B b   L l   M m   S s

M m   L l   K k   S s   G g

4 Review the middle letter sounds. Write the *middle* lower case letter for each picture.

B b   G g   M m   D d   V v

5 Practice reading these beginning blends. Use the short vowel sound.

l + a = la	l + o = lo	l + e = le	l + i = li
m + a = ma	m + e = me	m + i = mi	m + o = mo
m + u = mu	s + a = sa	s + e = se	s + o = so

Horizons® Phonics & Reading Grade 1 Student Book One

6 Add the ending sounds.

lă___	lŏ___	lĕ___	lĭ___	mă___	mĕ___
lab	lob	led	lid	mass	men
lad	Lon	Len	lit	mad	mess
lam	lot	let		mat	met

mŏ___	mŭ___	să___	sĭ___	sŏ___	sŭ___
mob	mud	sad	Sid	sob	sum
mod	mum	Sal	sin	sod	sun
mom	mutt	Sam	sit		sub

7 Practice reading these ending blends. Use the short vowel sound.

| u + m = um | u + d = ud | u + t = ut | u + s = us |

8 Add the beginning sounds.

___ŭm	___ŭd	___ŭt	___ŭs
bum	bud	but	bus
hum	dud	hut	fuss
mum	mud	mutt	muss
sum		nut	

Draw a line to match the pictures to the words.

bib

bed

mess

hat

bus

dad

hen

hot

fat

fuss

1 Draw a *circle* around the pictures that have the sound of short ă.

2 Draw a *square* around the pictures that have the sound of short ĕ.

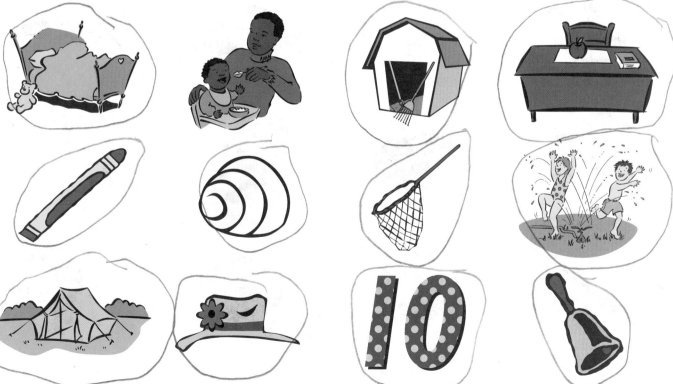

3 Draw an **X** through the pictures that have the sound of short ĭ.

4 *Underline* the pictures that have the short sound of ŏ.

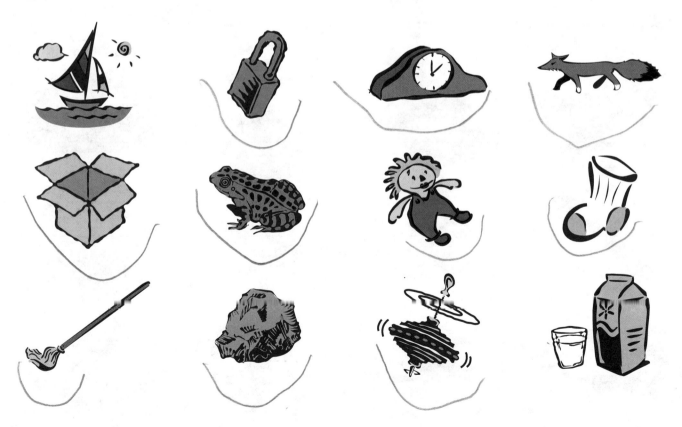

Horizons® Phonics & Reading Grade 1 Student Book One

5 *Circle* the pictures that have the short sound of ŭ.

6 Draw lines to match the short vowel words with their pictures.

hat
bat
fat

pig
dip
pin

pot
doll
dot

jet
net
nut

cut
mug
but

bus
run
sun

Read the list of words. Write each word under the correct short vowel sound.

Word List

~~bed~~	~~hen~~	~~lab~~	~~met~~	~~pig~~
~~bib~~	~~hot~~	~~lid~~	~~mop~~	~~sod~~
~~cat~~	~~hut~~	~~mad~~	~~mud~~	~~sum~~

Short ă

cat
lab
mad

Short ĕ

bed
hen
met

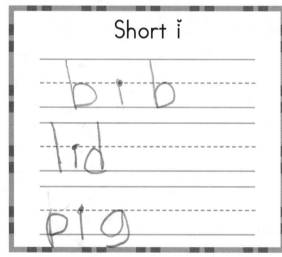

Short ĭ

bib
lid
pig

Short ŏ

hot
mop
sod

Short ŭ

hut
sum
mud

Horizons® Phonics & Reading Grade 1 Student Book One

1 Draw a *circle* around the pictures that have the long $\bar{a}$ sound. Long $\bar{a}$ says its name.

2 Draw a *square* around the pictures that have the long $\bar{e}$ sound. Long $\bar{e}$ says its name.

Draw an X through the pictures that have the long ī sound. Long ī says its name.

 Underline **the pictures that have the long ō sound. Long ō says its name.**

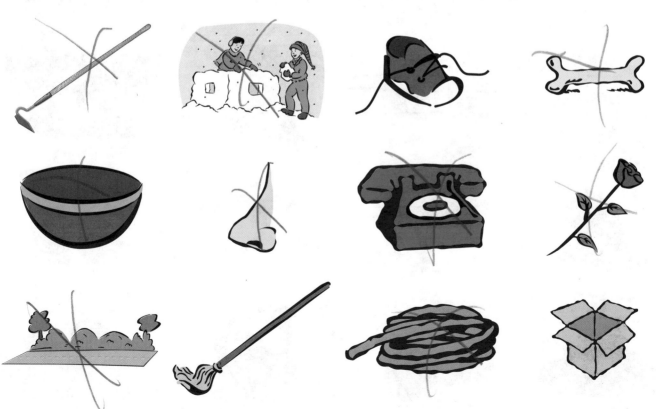

5   *Circle* the pictures that have the long u̅ sound. Long u̅ says its name.

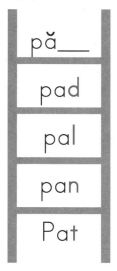 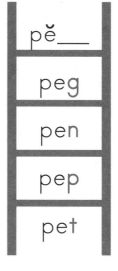 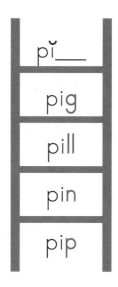

6   Practice reading these beginning blends. Use the short vowel sound.

p + a = pa	p + o = po	p + e = pe	p + i = pi	p + u = pu
r + a = ra	r + o = ro	r + e = re	r + i = ri	r + u = ru

7   Add the ending sounds.

pă___	pŏ___	pĕ___	pĭ___	pŭ___
pad	pod	peg	pig	pub
pal	pog	pen	pill	pug
pan	pop	pep	pin	pun
Pat	pot	pet	pip	pup

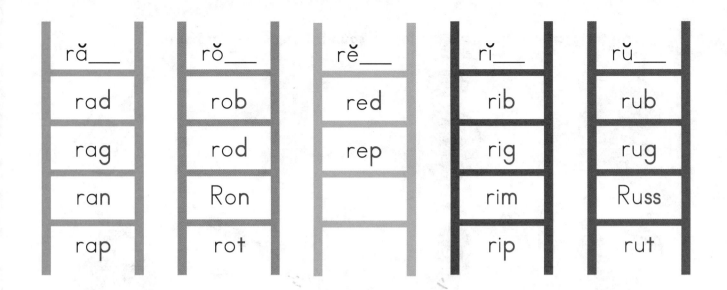

ră___	rŏ___	rĕ___	rĭ___	rŭ___
rad	rob	red	rib	rub
rag	rod	rep	rig	rug
ran	Ron		rim	Russ
rap	rot		rip	rut

8 Practice reading these ending blends. Use the short vowel sound.

a + p = ap	o + p = op	e + p = ep	i + p = ip	u + p = up

9 Add the beginning sounds.

___ăp	___ŏp	___ĕp	___ĭp	___ŭp
cap	bop	pep	dip	up
gap	cop	rep	hip	cup
lap	nop		Kip	pup
nap	top		sip	sup

Horizons® Phonics & Reading Grade 1 Student Book One

Rule:

In words that have a *vowel*, a *consonant*, and an e at the end, the first vowel sound is long and the e is silent. Examples: *tāpe̸*, *rīde̸*, *bōne̸*, and *tūbe̸*.

1 Read the short vowel words. Add a *silent e*, cross it out, and make a straight line over the vowel to show that it has the long sound. Read the words to your teacher.

rīpe̸	pīne̸	kīte̸	pāne̸
fīne̸	rīde̸	hīde̸	bīte̸
cūte̸	tōte̸	cūbe̸	dīme̸
tōne̸	hōpe̸	mōpe̸	rōde̸
rōbe̸	cāpe̸	tāpe̸	māte̸
rāte̸	māde̸	fāde̸	tūbe̸

2 Look at the pictures. Add a *silent e* to each word, cross it out, and make a straight line over the vowel to show that it has the long sound.

b̄onĕ   c̄akĕ   k̄itĕ   p̄latĕ

r̄obĕ   c̄onĕ   m̄ulĕ   r̄opĕ

Horizons® Phonics & Reading Grade 1 Student Book One

Practice reading these beginning blends. Use the short vowel sound.

j + a = ja	j + o = jo	j + e = je	j + i = ji	j + u = ju

 Add the ending sounds.

jă___	jŏ___	jě___	jĭ___	jŭ___
jab	job	Jeb	jib	jug
Jan	jog	Jed	jif	jut
jax	Jon	Jen	Jim	
	jot	jet	Jip	

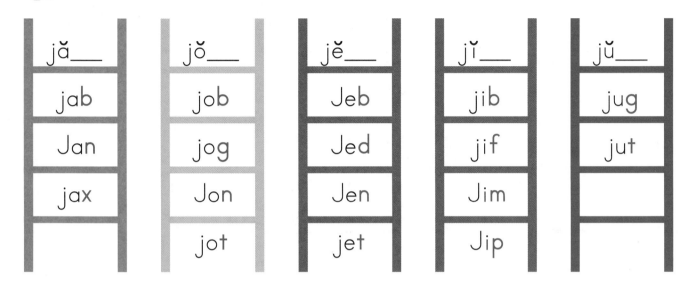 **Practice reading these beginning blends. Use the short vowel sound.**

v + a = va v + o = vo	v + e = ve v + i = vi	w + a = wa w + o = wo	w + e = we w + i = wi

 Add the ending sounds.

vă___	vŏ___	vě___	vĭ___
vac	Von	vet	vim
van	vox	vex	
vat			

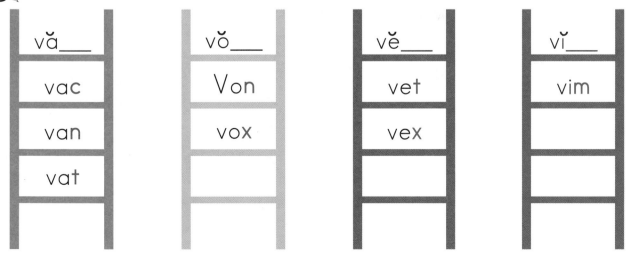

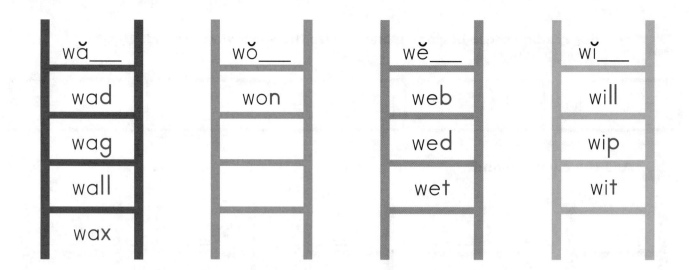

wă___
wad
wag
wall
wax

wŏ___
won

wĕ___
web
wed
wet

wĭ___
will
wip
wit

7 Practice reading these beginning blends. Use the short vowel sound.

y + a = ya	y + e = ye	z + e = ze
y + o = yo	z + a = za	z + i = zi

8 Add the ending sounds.

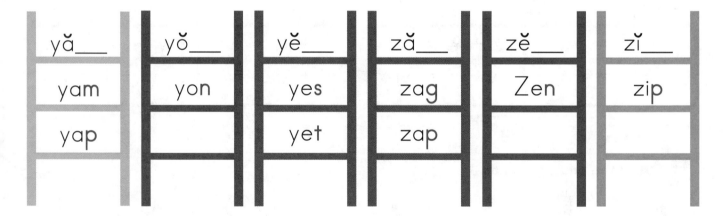

yă___
yam
yap

yŏ___
yon

yĕ___
yes
yet

ză___
zag
zap

zĕ___
Zen

zĭ___
zip

Hard & Soft Sounds of
c & g

Name: _____

Rule:

When *c* is followed by *e, i,* or *y,* it makes the soft sound as in the word *city*. When *c* is followed by *a, u,* or *o,* or a *consonant*, it makes the hard sound as in the word *cat*.

Underline the pictures that have the sound of *hard c*. Draw a *circle* around the pictures that have the *soft c* sound.

Rule:

When *g* is followed by *e, i* or *y*, it makes the *soft* sound as in the word *giraffe*. When *g* is followed by *a, u,* or *o*, or a *consonant*, it makes the *hard* sound as in the word *gum*.

2 *Underline* the pictures that have the sound of *soft g*. Draw a *square* around the pictures that have the sound of *hard g*.

Horizons® Phonics & Reading Grade 1 Student Book One

3 Use the words from the list to complete the crossword puzzle.

face   cane   gems   cake   gum   slice

ACROSS:
1.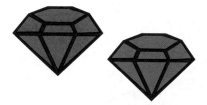
2.
3.
5.

DOWN:
1.
4.

Practice reading these ending blends. Use the short vowel sound.

e + v = ev	a + x = ax	o + x = ox
e + x = ex	i + x = ix	u + x = ux

5 **Add the beginning sounds.**

___ěv	___ăx	___ŏx	___ěx	___ĭx	___ŭx
Bev	ax	ox	hex	Dix	lux
	fax	box	Rex	fix	tux
	lax	fox	Tex	mix	
	Max	lox	vex	nix	
	sax	nox		pix	
	tax	pox		six	
	wax	sox			
		vox			

Consonant Digraphs
th, ch, wh

Name:

Rule:

A consonant digraph is two consonants that stay together to make their special sound. Consonant digraph *th* can be used at the beginning, middle, or end of a word. Examples: *thin*, *father*, and *path*. Consonant digraph *ch* can be used at the beginning or end of a word. Examples: *chin* and *such*. Consonant digraph *wh* makes the sound you hear in *when* and *whip*.

1 Look at the pictures below. Circle the correct consonant digraph to show whether the sound is at the *beginning* or at the *end* of the word.

| th | th | th | th | th | th | th | th |

| ch | ch | ch | ch | ch | ch | ch | ch |

2 Print the beginning sound under each picture that starts with consonant digraph *wh*.

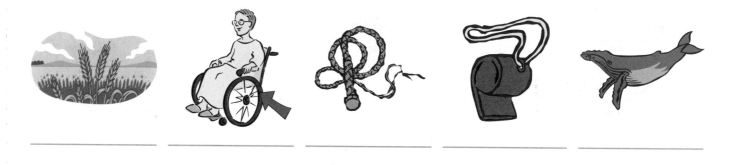

_____ _____ _____ _____ _____

3 Look at the pictures below. Circle the correct beginning consonant digraph.

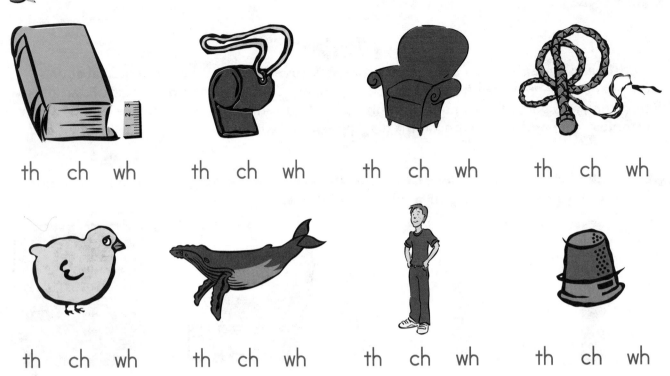

th   ch   wh   th   ch   wh   th   ch   wh   th   ch   wh

th   ch   wh   th   ch   wh   th   ch   wh   th   ch   wh

4 Look at the pictures. Complete the words by writing the *th* at the beginning, the middle, or the end of each word.

fa ___ er mo ___ er pa ___

___ ick ___ in ba ___

Horizons® Phonics & Reading Grade 1 Student Book One

Read each sentence. Use the words from the list to complete the sentences.

Word List

chums	chess	chill	much	chop	chat

1. Jill and Kim are _____ .

2. They like each other very _____ .

3. They like to bake, and they like to play _____ .

4. They _____ with each other as they play.

5. Dad had to _____ logs for the fireplace.

6. He did not want us to get a _____ .

Look at the pictures. Complete the words by writing the *ch* at the beginning or the end of each word.

pin _____   lun _____   _____ at

7 Add *th* to each of the words below, then read the words to your teacher.

wi _____   mo _____   _____ in   _____ ud

pa _____   ma _____   _____ is   _____ at

8 Add *ch* to each of the words below, then read the words to your teacher.

_____ in   _____ aff   _____ ip   _____ ap

su _____   _____ ug   ri _____   mu _____

9 Add *wh* to each of the words below, then read the words to your teacher.

_____ ip   _____ iff   _____ im   _____ am

_____ en   _____ et   _____ ip   _____ iz

Vowel Pairs
ai, ay, ee, ea

Name:
_____
_____

Rule:

A vowel pair is two vowels that come together to make one long vowel sound. The first vowel is long, and the second vowel is silent. Examples: *ai/rain, ay/say, ee/tree,* and *ea/read.*

Say the name for each picture. Finish the words under each picture with the correct vowel pair.

s _____ l   p _____ nt   p l _____   s w _____ p

b _____   t r _____   r _____ n   c r _____ k

t _____   t h r _____ d   s l _____ p t   _____ m

2 Write the name of each picture. Use the words from the list.

Word List							
team	seat	leaf	seal	tree	peek	tray	rain

_____

_____

_____

_____

_____

_____

_____

_____

3 Add long ē before the vowel each word to make a new word with the long ē sound.

ten _____

_____

sat _____

_____

mat _____

_____

cram _____

4 Add *ay* to each of the words below, then read the words to your teacher.

pl _____ pr _____ tr _____ h _____

st _____ m _____ J _____ gr _____

5 Draw lines to match the pictures with the words.

teeth

seal

tree

feet

meat

bee

eagle

sleep

team

sweep

6 Underline the word that completes each sentence. Write it on the line.

1. _____ like to go to the zoo.

    keep   we   two

2. The _____ are fun to see.

    seals   those   stay

3. I like the _____ best.

    tree   eagle   make

4. We rest under a shade_____.

    box   tree   have

5. We use the benches for_____.

    tent   fell   seats

6. Our _____ get tired after lots of walking.

    feet   not   time

7. We will _____ the lions next.

    read   see   tree

8. They have big _____.

    hat   day   teeth

9. Then we will_____ have a cold drink.

    teach   each   come

10. We will come_____ the animals again soon!

    see   then   great

Vowel Pairs
ie, oa, oe

Name:

Rule:

A vowel pair is two vowels that come together to make one long vowel sound. The first vowel is long, and the second vowel is silent. Examples: *ie/pie, oa/boat,* and *oe/toe.*

1. Read the name under each picture. Draw a straight line over the long vowel and draw a line through the silent vowel. Example: hōé

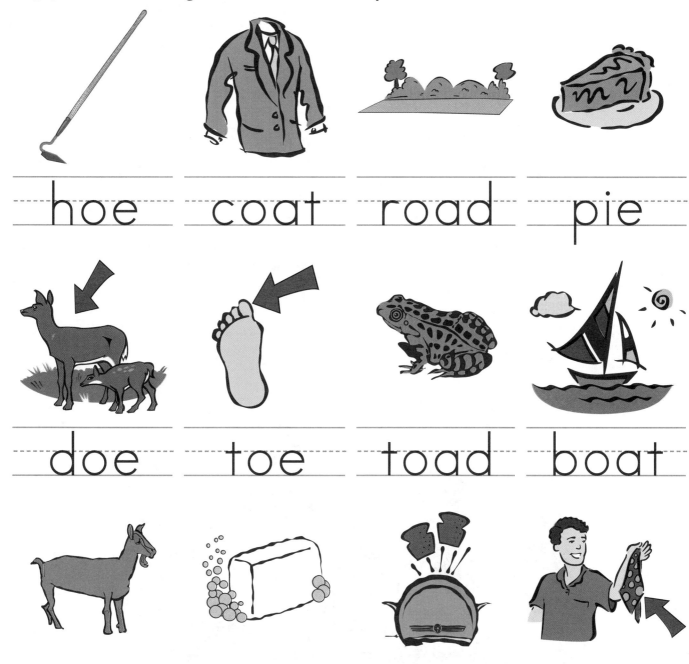

hoe   coat   road   pie

doe   toe   toad   boat

goat   soap   toast   tie

2 Add *oa* to each of the words below, then read the words to your teacher.

t___ ___d fl___ ___t J___ n___ r___ d___

r___ stt___ sts___ p___ g___ ___t

3 Add *oe* to each of the words below, then read the words to your teacher.

t___ h___ J___ d___

4 Add *ie* to each of the words below, then read the words to your teacher.

l___ p___ d___ t___

1 Write the beginning consonant sound for each picture.

----

2 Write the ending consonant sound for each picture.

Write the middle consonant sound for each picture.

_____

- - - - - - - - - - - - - - - - -

_____

- - - - - - - - - - - - - - - - -

 Draw lines to match the pictures with the words.

mail

ice

wheel

goat

cube

fan

lips

shell

clock

lunch

5 **Underline the word that completes each sentence. Write it on the line.**

1. sat
   Sam
   map

   My dog is _____ .

2. brown
   jump
   man

   He is _____ .

3. bed
   play
   can

   He likes to _____ .

4. fat
   bib
   park

   We go to the _____ .

5. wind
   mitt
   sat

   I take my _____ .

6. wig
   pig
   ball

   My dog and I play _____ .

7. tap
   runs
   nap

   My dog _____ as fast as he can.

8. bath
   get
   gas

   He likes to _____ the ball.

9. jet
   school
   tan

   One day I took my dog to _____ .

10. ball
    pet
    tell

    We were having "show and _____ ."

11. pet
    liked
    ham

    The kids liked to _____ my dog.

6 Read the short vowel words. Add a *silent e*, cross it out, and make a straight line over the vowel to show that it has the long sound.

1. Add silent e̸ to fin: _____

2. Add silent e̸ to rob: _____

3. Add silent e̸ to mad: _____

4. Add silent e̸ to cut: _____

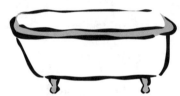

5. Add silent e̸ to tub: _____

6. Add silent e̸ to bit: _____

7. Add silent e̸ to dim: _____

8. Add silent e̸ to tap: _____

Horizons® Phonics & Reading Grade 1 Student Book One

Rules:

A sentence is a complete thought that tells *who did what*. Every sentence must start with a capital letter and end with a period (.) at the end of a statement, a question mark (?) at the end of a question, or an exclamation mark (!) to show excitement or a command.

1 Read the sentences. Write a *period* if the sentence is a statement, a *question mark* if the sentence is a question, or an *exclamation mark* if the sentence shows excitement.

1. My dog likes bones____

2. I am seven years old____

3. How old are you____

4. I love my mom and dad____

5. Look out for that car____

6. Mike likes to eat chips____

7. Wow____ Look at that____

8. What is your name____

9. Will you be my pal____

10. Stop____ Come back____

. ? ! . ? / . ? ! . ? / . ? !

Rule:

An abbreviation is a short form of a word. A period (.) is used after an abbreviation. **Examples:** *Mr.* and *Mrs.*

2 Read the sentence and copy it on the lines below. Add the correct punctuation.

Mr and Mrs Dix will meet with Mr Jones today

_____

_____

_____

Rules:

A capital letter is used at the beginning of every sentence. Names also begin with a capital letter as in _Ann_ and _Bob_.

3 Read the sentences and copy them on the lines below. Use the correct capitalization and punctuation.

sam and i will go to a ball game

_____

will ed and jim go with us

_____

mr jones will take us to the game

_____

do you want a hot dog

_____

wow   he hit a home run

_____

we had a nice day with mr jones

_____

Review:
Long-Vowel &
Short-Vowel Sounds

Name:

Rules:

When a word or syllable has two vowels, the first vowel is usually *long*, and the second vowel is usually *silent* as in *kite*, *pain*, *weep*, *blue*, and *pay*.

When a word has one vowel, the vowel usually has the short sound as in *bet*, *hat*, and *cot*.

Put the words from the list into the correct categories.

Word List

coat	rob	mess	week	wig	cot	dime	zap	white
eat	fail	lid	flute	rate	rat	fed	blue	toe

Long ā

Long ē

Long ī

Long ō

Long ū

Short ă

Short ě

Short ǐ

Short ǒ

2

Draw lines to match the words that rhyme.

pain	moat
eat	tie
boat	bake
bike	gain
lake	line
flute	dime
game	cute
pine	treat
time	like
pie	lame

Draw lines to match the words with the same vowel sounds.

plane	deal
thug	wet
tin	run
tune	June
cat	got
fun	Jane
wheel	lug
cot	win
get	that

Horizons® Phonics & Reading Grade 1 Student Book One

clock

pine

lid

flute

wheel

van

cane

cat

frog

duck

5 Now write a sentence using at least three of the words from above.

- -

6 **Underline the word that completes each sentence. Write it on the line.**

1. and
   bus
   are

   Jim rides a _____ to class.

2. bus
   school
   too

   He likes _____ very much.

3. desk
   car
   tan

   Jim sits at a _____ .

4. turn
   fun
   reads

   In the morning, he _____ books.

5. math
   path
   bath

   In the afternoon, he works on _____ .

6. best
   try
   wig

   Mike is Jim's _____ pal.

7. rain
   play
   pan

   They like to _____ outside.

8. took
   tag
   try

   Jim and Mike like to play _____ .

9. cat
   man
   sit

   At lunch, they _____ togothor.

10. glad
    car
    green

    Jim is _____ that he has such a
    good pal.

Horizons® Phonics & Reading Grade 1 Student Book One

Rule:

A compound word is a word made from two or more words joined together to make one word, as in *backyard*, *runway*, or *mailbox*.

✏ **Write the two words that make up the compound word.**

doghouse

backyard

sunlight

scarecrow

cupcake

railroad

raincoat

myself

popcorn

peanut

2 Choose the correct compound word that goes with the clue.

Word List

| mailbox | backpack | cupcake | popcorn | sailboat |

1. A box for mail is a _____ .

2. A cake that comes in a cup is a _____ .

3. Corn that you pop is _____ .

4. A boat that sails is a _____ .

5. A pack that goes
   on your back is called a _____ .

3 **Use the words from the list to complete the crossword puzzle.**

doghouse   sandbox   sailboats   seaweed   scarecrow

ACROSS:

1. You can race on the sea in these.
3. Farmers sometimes put this in their fields to keep the birds away.
4. A place for a dog to sleep.

DOWN:

2. A plant that grows in the sea.
3. You can play with sand in this.

4 Underline the compound word that completes each sentence. Write it on the line.

1. It was time for Mike to eat _____.

   mailbox   breakfast   cans

2. His mom made _____.

   trucks   pancakes   stores

3. Mike was playing in the_____.

   uphill   grape   backyard

4. His mother called him_____.

   keep   inside   around

5. He asked her if he could eat _____.

   mine   table   outside

6. Mike got to eat_____.

   over   outdoors   are

7. He also ate a_____.

   cupcake   kite   raincoat

8. Next time, he will have _____.

   may   oatmeal   mailbox

Rule:

A word is *plural* if it means "more than one." Example: *trucks, cars, plates,* **and** *things.*

1 Circle the picture of the things that are more than one.

2 Write two sentences. Use words that name some of the pictures from above.

Rule:

When a word ends in *ss*, *ch*, *sh*, or *x*, you usually add *es* at the end to make the word plural.

3 **Write the plural form of each word.**

dress _____   lunch _____

class _____   crash _____

box _____   glass _____

brush _____   fox _____

peach _____   church _____

4 **Write a sentence using two of the words from above. Draw a picture to go with your sentence.**

_____

_____

_____

Rule:

When a word ends in a vowel plus y, you usually add -s at the end to make the word plural.

5 Write the plural form of each word.

turkey _____   donkey _____

monkey _____   chimney _____

jay _____

toy _____

play _____

6 Write the base word for each of the plural words.

dresses _____   foxes _____

churches _____   classes _____

toys _____

turkeys _____

brushes _____

Rule:

When a word ends in *f* or *fe*, change the *f* to a *v* and *es* to make the word plural, as in *leaf/leaves*, *elf/elves*, and *wife/wives*.

7 Write the plural form of each word.

leaf _____

shelf _____

elf _____

half _____

life _____

wife _____

knife _____

wolf _____

calf _____

scarf _____

Suffixes in
Short-Vowel Words

Name:

Rule:

A suffix is an ending that is added to a base word. Many words do not have to have their spelling changed before a suffix is added.

1 Make a new word by adding the suffixes *-s*, *-ed*, or *-ing*. Write the new words on the lines.

-s	-ed	-ing
rain		
lift		
clean		
mend		
open		
peek		

Rule:

Base words are words that do not have a *prefix* (beginning) or a *suffix* (ending) added to them.

2 Write the base word for each of the following words.

raining _____   opened _____

played _____   mending _____

cleaning _____

Rule:

The suffix -er is used to compare two things. The suffix -est is used to compare more than two things. Examples: "Sue is *shorter* than her sister" (comparing two things). "She is the *shortest* in her family" (comparing more than two things).

3 Read each sentence. Add -er or -est to the word shown under the line. Then write the new word on the line.

1. Bill is _____ than his brother, Jeff.
    tall

2. Jeff is _____ than Bill.
    short

3. Jeff is _____ than Bill.
    old

4. Bill is the _____ member of the family.
    tall

5. He is also the _____ .
    young

Rule:

The suffix -er sometimes means "a person who." Example: someone who works is a *worker*. A person who sings is a *singer*.

4 Add the suffix -er to each word. Write the new word on the line.

jump _____   climb _____

paint _____   bake _____

Rule:

If a word with a short vowel ends in a single consonant, you usually double the consonant before adding a suffix that begins with a vowel. Examples: *tag/tagged, tagging; big/bigger, biggest; fat/fatter, fattest.*

5 **Add the suffix *-ed* to make new words.**

rip _____   stop _____

beg _____   tip _____

fan _____

6 **Add the suffix *-er* to make new words.**

hot _____   win _____

flat _____   run _____

bat _____

7 **Add the suffix *-est* or *-ing* to make new words.**

hot _____   flat _____

glad _____   win _____

run _____   spin _____

8 **Read each sentence. Add the correct suffix to the word under the line. Then write the new word on the line.**

1. Today was the _____ day of summer.
   hot

2. We went _____ .
   swim

3. Jimmy made the _____ splash.
   big

4. He is the _____ one of all of us.
   short

5. We had fun _____ in the pond.
   play

6. We laughed when a frog _____ by Jimmy's foot.
   hop

7. I tried _____ like the frog.
   skip

8. When we went home, we all _____ .
   nap

9 **What would you do on a hot day? Write your answer below.**

_____

- -

_____

- -

_____

Suffixes in
Silent e Words

Name: _____

Rule:

If a word ends in silent **e**, drop the **e** before adding a suffix that begins with a vowel.
Examples: *bake/baking, write/writer, slice/slicing*.

1. Add the suffixes *-es*, *-er*, or *-est* to each word. Write the new words on the lines.

bake _____ , _____

take _____ , _____

make _____ , _____

dive _____ , _____

slice _____ , _____

cute _____ , _____

2. Now write the base word for each word below.

shining _____   writer _____

bravest _____   bakes _____

hoping _____   smiles _____

used _____   hiding _____

3
Read each sentence. Add the correct suffix to each word under the lines. Then write the new word on the lines.

1. Jill was _____ cookies.
   bake

2. Her pal Kim was _____ them with her.
   make

3. They _____ a wooden spoon to mix things.
   use

4. Mom _____ as she watched them.
   smile

5. She _____ the cookies would be good.
   hope

6. The girls were _____ turns adding things.
   take

7. Mom _____ the way they shared the spoon.
   like

8. Jill and Kim were being safe by _____ Mom
   have
   use the stove.

4
What foods or meals have you helped to make? Tell about them on the lines below.

_____

_____

_____

_____

Rule:

A suffix is an ending that is added to a base word to make a new word. Usually when the suffixes *-ful*, *-ly*, *-less*, or *-ness* are added, the spelling of the base word does not change. Examples: *painful, sadness, hopeless, quickly*.

1 Make new words by adding *-ful*, *-ly*, *-less*, or *-ness* to the base words.

hope _____ , _____

use _____ , _____

kind _____ , _____

care _____ , _____

glad _____ , _____

2 Read each sentence. Add the suffix *-ful*, *-ly*, *-less*, or *-ness* to the base word. Write the new word on the line in the sentence.

1. Mary had to be _____ riding her bike.
   care

2. She wanted to ride _____ .
   safe

3. Her mom _____ helped her to get on her bike.
   glad

4. Mary's bike was very _____ .
   color

3 Write the base word for each of the words below.

neatness _____

badly _____

thankful _____

careless _____

spoonful _____

loudly _____

goodness _____

sickness _____

hopeful _____

4 Write a sentence using at least two of the words from above.

_____

_____

_____

_____

Rule:

A consonant digraph is two consonants that stay together to make their special sound. Consonant digraph *sh* can be used at the beginning or end of a word, as in *shed* and *hash*.

5 Look at the pictures. Finish the words under each picture with the *sh* sound.

wi_____   ru_____   _____ed   _____ut

6 Look at the pictures below. Circle the correct *sh* to show whether the *sh* sound is at the *beginning* or at the *end* of the word.

sh   sh   sh   sh   sh   sh   sh   sh

sh   sh   sh   sh   sh   sh   sh   sh

7 Draw lines to match the words that rhyme.

shell	hut
cash	hash
shut	fish
wish	gush
ship	rip
rush	tell

8 Add *sh* to each of the words below, then read the words to your teacher.

_____ in _____ am _____ un _____ da

ma _____ ag _____ ed _____ mu _____

Horizons® Phonics & Reading Grade 1 Student Book One

Suffixes -y, -en, -able,
Consonant Blends cl, cr

Name: _____

Rule:

When a word ends in a single or a double consonant, the spelling does not usually need to be changed when adding the suffixes *-y*, *-en*, or *-able*. Examples: *frost/frosty*, *dark/darken*, *wear/wearable*.

1 Add the suffix *-y* to make new words.

wind _____   hand _____

trick _____   dust _____

speed _____

2 Add the suffix *-en* to make new words.

weak _____   hard _____

dark _____   loose _____

sharp _____

3 Add the suffix *-able* to make new words.

crush _____   sink _____

suit _____   drink _____

break _____

Horizons® Phonics & Reading Grade 1 Student Book One

4 **Read each word and write its base word on the line beside it.**

soften _____   dusty _____

drinkable _____   sticky _____

wearable _____

5 **Read each sentence. Choose the correct word to complete the sentence. Write the word on the line.**

1. The vase is very _____ .

    valuable   drinkable

2. It is made of _____ glass.

    darken   breakable

3. It is only _____ to look at.

    suitable   sinkable

4. Sometimes it gets _____ on the shelf.

    frosty   dusty

Rule:

A consonant blend is two consonants that work together at the beginning or ending of a word. Each consonant says its own sound. In consonant blend *cl*, c and *l* blend together to make the sound you hear in *class*. In consonant blend *cr*, c and *r* blend together to make the sound you hear in *crib*.

 6 Look at the pictures. Finish the words under each picture with the *cl* sound.

_____ ass   _____ iff   _____ ap   _____ ock

7 Add *cl* to each of the words below, then read the words to your teacher.

_____ am   _____ an   _____ ef   _____ od

_____ og   _____ op   _____ ip   _____ ub

8 Add *cr* to each of the words below, then read the words to your teacher.

_____ am   _____ ag   _____ ib   _____ oss

_____ op   _____ ab

9 **Read each sentence. Choose the correct word to complete the sentence. Then write the word on the line.**

1. Be careful when you _____ the road.

   cross   class

2. It is time to go to _____ .

   clap   class

3. Mom had a _____ in the sink.

   crop   clog

4. Jan looked at the _____ to tell the time.

   clot   clock

5. The baby sleeps in a _____ .

   club   crib

6. We will hike to the top of the _____ .

   cliff   clef

Review:
Plurals & Suffixes,
Consonant Blends bl, br

Name: ----------------------------------

1 Read each sentence. Choose the correct word to complete the sentence. Then write the word on the line.

1. Julie's family was _____ to move.

   going   opening

2. They were _____ their boxes.

   reading   packing

3. They had been _____ for a house for months.

   looking   helping

4. Moving day was the _____ day of the year.

   coldest   farmer

5. Julie stayed in the truck where it was _____.

   warmer   jumping

6. She knew she would soon be _____.

   printing   helping

2 The following plural words are spelled incorrectly. Write the correct spelling on the line next to each word. Remember: *plural* means more than one!

Word List				
churches	wolves	jays	toys	foxes

foxs _____   wolfs _____

chursches _____   jais _____

toies _____

Use the words from the list to complete the crossword puzzle.

wives   glasses   snowy   leaves   smoothest

ACROSS:
2. Husbands have ____ .
4. The water on the lake is the ____ when it isn't windy.
5. The day was cold and ____ .

DOWN:
1. She has trouble seeing, so she needs ____ .
3. In the fall, trees drop their ____ .

4 **Circle the plural words that are correctly spelled.**

1. toys
   toies

2. boxes
   boxxs

3. dresses
   dresss

4. brushs
   brushes

5. elfs
   elves

6. churchs
   churches

5 **Read the poem. Choose the correct words from the list to complete the poem.**

Some bugs are _____ .

They have wings.

Some bugs are _____ .

They have other things.

Some bugs are _____

And covered with a shell.

Some bugs even have

A way to make them smell!

But no matter how _____

Or _____ they are,

I like bugs and I keep them in a jar!

Word List

crawling

smelly

flying

hairy

harder

Rule:

A consonant blend is two consonants that work together at the beginning or ending of a word. Each consonant says its own sound. In consonant blend *bl*, *b* and *l* blend together to make the sound you hear in *bless*. In consonant blend *br*, *b* and *r* blend together to make the sound you hear in *brush*.

6 Add *bl* to each of the words below, then read the words to your teacher.

eed   ess   iss   ank

ot   uff   eat   ame

7 Add *br* to each of the words below, then read the words to your teacher.

im   ag   at   ush

and   ink   ibe   oke

Rule Review:

A vowel pair is two vowels that come together to make one long vowel sound. The first vowel is long, and the second vowel is silent. Examples: *oa/boat; ee/meet; ie/tie; ay/say; ai/train; ea/teach.*

Read each sentence. Choose the correct word to complete the sentence. Write the word on the line.

1. Mary wanted to _____ her brother to skate.
   teach   tree

2. Mary _____ to show him.
   may   tried

3. He didn't _____ like listening.
   feel   show

4. He wanted to _____ pie.
   good   eat

5. They decided to try again next _____.
   week   sail

Read each sentence. Underline the word with a vowel pair in each sentence.

1. We like to feed the ducks.

2. They eat the crumbs we give them.

3. We sit under the trees.

4. We put our feet into the water.

5. We watch toads jump along the grassy banks.

3 Read each riddle. Choose the correct word from the list to answer each riddle. Write the word on the line.

Word List

wheels	train	tie	eat	play	leaves

1. We do this with shoelaces.

2. This runs on tracks.

3. These grow on trees.

4. We do this at recess.

5. Trains have these.

6. We do this with food.

4 Now make up a riddle of your own. Have your teacher help you write it down.

1. Look at each picture. Write and mark the vowel sound for each picture.

2. Write the two words that make up each compound word.

backyard

mailbox

sunshine

sailboat

cupcake

today

3 Write the plural form of each word.

dress _____   brush _____

fox _____   class _____

wolf _____   church _____

4 Write the base word for these words with suffixes.

jumping _____   hottest _____

taller _____   hopped _____

farmer _____   petting _____

used _____   hiding _____

safest _____   baker _____

shining _____   chasing _____

5 Read each sentence. Underline the words containing the vowel pairs *oa, ee, ie, ai, ay* or *ea.*

1. Jill likes to paint.

2. She painted a picture of a pie.

3. The pie looked so real, she wanted to eat it!

4. After that, she went outside to play.

Rule:

Vowel digraphs are two vowels put together in a word that make a long or short sound or have a special sound all their own. Vowel digraphs *au* and *aw* make the sounds you hear in *auto* and *saw*. Vowel digraph *ea* makes the short ĕ sound you hear in *head*. Vowel digraph *ei* makes the long ā sound you hear in *eight*. Vowel digraph *ew* makes the sound you hear in *new*. Vowel digraph *oo* makes the sound you hear in *book* or in *pool*.

1 Read each sentence. Circle the words that have the vowel digraphs *oo, ea, au, aw, ei,* or *ew*.

1. Mary looked at the clock and saw that it was noon.

2. She read eight pages in a book and then went out.

3. It was cool outside, so she put on her new sweater.

4. She stood in the sun and saw a bird as it flew overhead.

2 Read each word in the word list. Then write the words in the correct categories.

Word List

pool	bread	school	heavy	look
book	dread	took	tool	

oo as in good	oo as in cool	ea as in head

3 Choose the correct word to complete each sentence. Print the words on the lines.

1. She _____ the shawl over her head.

   then   threw

2. Did Paul _____ his food?

   head   chew

3. The _____ was very good on a cold day.

   stew   yawn

4 Read the story. Complete the story using words from the list.

Word List

| good | look | books | crawl | yawn |

I like to read _____ . They are _____ .

When I _____ into bed
at night, my mom reads to me.

I _____ when the story is done because I am tired.

I _____ forward to reading another one!

5 Add *fl* to each of the words below, then read the words to your teacher.

ag   ew   ap   at

op   aw   ood   ip

Review:
Vowel Pairs &
Vowel Digraphs

Name: _____

Rules:

A *vowel pair* has two vowels put together to make one long vowel sound. The first vowel makes the long sound, and the second vowel is silent.

A *vowel digraph* has two vowels put together in a word that make a long or short sound or have a special sound all their own.

✏ **Write the words from the list in the correct categories.**

Word List

rain	tie	book	saw	weigh
street	head	say	caught	eat

Vowel Pairs

Vowel Digraphs

Write a short story using words from the list below.

Word List				
boat	wheel	book	saw	
play	eat	ready	laundry	eight

_____

- -

_____

- -

_____

- -

_____

- -

_____

- -

Draw a picture about your story.

Jim likes to play soccer. His team is called the Rams. They practice every Friday afternoon after school. Jim is the goal keeper for his team. He guards the net to make sure that the other team does not get a goal.

The team plays their games on Saturday mornings. One time, they made eight goals in a game! Jim did a good job of guarding his team's net that day. The other team made only three goals.

1. What sport does Jim play?

2. What is the name of his team?

3. On what day of the week do they practice?

4. What position does Jim play?

5. How many points did Jim's team score in one of their games.

coat	toad	keep	weight
pie	claw	each	pause

```
r  e  p  i  e  c  k  r  s
o  n  e  f  s  k  e  e  p
w  e  i  g  h  t  a  i  r
a  o  c  a  c  s  c  r  i
s  z  p  r  l  s  h  a  t
t  o  c  o  a  t  r  u  p
e  e  m  t  w  o  s  w  a
t  a  l  c  r  a  w  k  u
r  s  e  e  r  d  o  p  s
s  a  m  t  o  t  r  i  e
```

Consonant Digraphs
bt, ph,
Consonant Blends dr, gr

Name: _____

Rules:

In consonant digraph *bt*, the *b* is silent and the *t* is pronounced as in *doubt* and *subtle*.
Consonant digraph *ph* makes the *f* sound as in *phone* and *elephant*.

1. Write the words from the list in the correct categories.

Word List

| telephone | doubt | digraph | subtle | elephant |

Digraph ph
_____
_____
_____
_____
_____
_____

Digraph bt
_____
_____
_____
_____

2. Read each sentence. Choose the word that completes the sentence and write it on the line.

1. Jack had no _____ that he would have fun at
the party.
with   doubt

2. He called his friend Jim on the _____ .
fish   telephone

3. Jim's phone was shaped like an _____ .
wheat   elephant

3 Add *gr* to each of the words below, then read the words to your teacher.

ill	ab	ip	ub
ain	eat	ope	ipe

4 Add *dr* to each of the words below, then read the words to your teacher.

ill	ab	ip	ain
ink	ew	ive	aw

5 Look at the pictures. Circle the consonant blend that makes the beginning sound you hear.

br cr dr gr   br cr dr gr   br cr dr gr   br cr dr gr

br cr dr gr   br cr dr gr   br cr dr gr   br cr dr gr

Rules:

In consonant digraph *gm*, the *g* is silent and the *m* is pronounced as in *diaphragm*.
In consonant digraph *mn*, the *n* is silent and the *m* is pronounced as in *column* and *solemn*.

1 Circle the consonants in the words. Cross out the silent consonants.

diaphragm	column	solemn	phlegm

2 Add *gl* to each of the words below, then read the words to your teacher.

_____ad _____ass _____op _____en

3 Look at the pictures. Circle the consonant blend that makes the beginning sound you hear.

gl fl sp   gl fl sp   gl fl sp   gl fl sp

4 Add *sp* to each of the words below, then read the words to your teacher.

_____ ill _____ in _____ ell _____ ot

_____ end wi _____ cla _____ gra _____

5 Look at the pictures. Circle the consonant blend that makes the *beginning* sound you hear.

gl   fl   sp   gl   fl   sp   gl   fl   sp   gl   fl   sp

6 Look at the pictures below. Circle the *sp* to show whether the sound is at the *beginning* or at the *end* of the word.

sp   sp   sp   sp   sp   sp   sp   sp

Lesson 25

Review:
Consonant Digraphs
& Consonant Blends

Name: _____

1 Circle the consonant digraphs in each of the words below.

column	doubt	patch
elephant	phlegm	diaphragm
phone	match	much

2 Read each sentence. Choose the word that completes the sentence and write it on the line.

1. Mike had no _____ that his team would win.
   doubt   match

2. Mitch has a _____ in his room.
   phlegm   phone

3. Add the numbers in the last _____ .
   diaphragm   column

4. Dad needs a _____ to light the fire.
   match   much

5. The tire on my bike is flat and needs a _____ .
   patch   match

6. We went to the zoo and saw a huge _____ .
   diaphragm   elephant

Look at the pictures. Finish the words under each picture by adding *ch* or *tch*.

_____ in   ca _____   pa _____   ma _____

 Look at the pictures. Circle the consonant blend that makes the sound you hear.

bl cl fl gl   bl cl fl gl   bl cl fl gl   bl cl fl gl

br cr dr gr   br cr dr gr   br cr dr gr   br cr dr gr

fl cl gr sp   br cl gr sp   br cl gr sp   br cl gr sp

90

Horizons® Phonics & Reading Grade 1 Student Book One

Name: _____

Rule:

A consonant digraph is two consonants that stay together to make their special sound. In consonant digraph *ck*, the *k* is pronounced and the *c* is silent as in *clock* and *check*.

✏ Look at the pictures. Finish the word under each picture with the ending consonant digraph *ck*.

ba   clo   chi

sti   du   ro

pa   che   tru

2 Read each sentence. Underline the word that completes the sentence. Write it on the line.

1. The boy went _____ to see his dog.

    back   now

2. He needed to _____ on him.

    can   check

3. He looked at the _____ .

    clock   came

4. The clock had a _____ in it.

    path   crack

3 Add *nd* to each of the words below, then read the words to your teacher.

be   se   bo   fo

ha   fu   te   ba

4 Add *nt* to each of the words below, then read the words to your teacher.

ce   hi   pa   ve

hu   se   pla   be

Rule:

A consonant digraph is two consonants that stay together to make their special sound.
Consonant digraph *gh* can make two sounds. The *gh* can be silent as in *weigh* and *night*.
The *gh* can also make the *f* sound as in *laugh*, *rough*, and *tough*.

1 Draw a line to match the pictures with the correct words.

weigh

night

rough

laugh

right

2 Read each sentence. Underline the word that completes the sentence. Write the word on the line.

1. Sam and his dad went to the circus at _____ .
night   then

2. Sam's dad drove _____ up to the circus tent.
trick   right

3. It wasn't _____ to find a parking space.
tough   try

4. Sam _____ at the clowns.
laughed   checked

5. He liked the_____ way that they played.
took   rough

3

Look at the pictures. Circle the consonant digraph or blend that makes the ending sound you hear.

gh ng nk	gh ng nk	gh ng nk	gh ng nk

gh ng nk	gh ng nk	gh ng nk	gh ng nk

4

Add *ng* to each of the words below, then read the words to your teacher.

lu	ga	ba	wi
su	zi	so	ha

5

Add *nk* to each of the words below, then read the words to your teacher.

cra	ho	ta	wi
du	ba	i	ju

Horizons® Phonics & Reading Grade 1 Student Book One

Name: _____

Rule Review:

Consonant digraph *gh* can make two sounds. The *gh* can be *silent* and can also make the *f* sound. In consonant digraph *ck*, the *k* is pronounced and the *c* is silent.
When two consonants are together at the end of a word, we blend them together, as in *tusk* and *desk*.

Use the words from the list to complete the crossword puzzle.

neck   clock   laugh   rough   night

ACROSS:
1. This is what comes after the sun goes down.
2. This tells you what time it is.
4. This is the opposite of smooth.

DOWN:
1. This is the part of your body that is below your head.
3. This is what you do when you think something is funny.

2 **Write three sentences. Use some of the words from the list.**

Word List							
bought	check	thick	brought	trick	thought	crack	track

1. _____

2. _____

3. _____

3 **Look at the pictures. Finish the words under each picture by adding the ending consonant blend _sk_ .**

de_____   tu_____   ta_____   ma_____

Put the words in alphabetical order.

Word List

| ask | laugh | tusk | check | fight | bright | neck | sink |

1. _____

2. _____

3. _____

4. _____

5. _____

6. _____

7. _____

8. _____

Use the words in the word list to complete the story.

Word List

necks	bought	laugh	thought	knocked	roughly

Dawn liked to go to the circus. She _____ that

the clowns were funny. They made her_____.

They always played so _____. They tumbled

around and _____ each other down. They wore

colorful collars around their _____. Dawn's

dad _____ her some popcorn.

Review: Consonant
Digraphs gn, ch, tch,
Consonant blends mp, lp

Name:
_____

Rules:

In consonant digraph *gn*, the *g* is silent and the *n* is pronounced as in *sign* and *align*.
Consonant digraph *ch* makes the beginning sound you hear in *chair*. It can also make the *k* sound as in *chorus*.

1 Draw a line to match the pictures to the words.

catch

sign

chorus

gnaw

chair

chin

2 Read the above words, then write the correct consonant digraphs in the blanks below.

cat_____   _____in   _____air

si_____   _____aw   _____orus

3 Use the words from the list to answer the questions.

Word List					
sign	chin	chair	chorus	sandwich	gnaw

1. What is the part of your face below your mouth? _____

2. What would your mom put in your lunch box? _____

3. What is on a street corner and tells drivers to stop? _____

4. What is a group of singers called? _____

5. What does a dog do to a bone? _____

4 Add *mp* to each of the words below, then read the words to your teacher.

lu _____ ca _____ li _____ da _____

ju _____ bu _____ la _____ hu _____

5 Add *lp* to each of the words below, then read the words to your teacher.

gu _____ he _____ ke _____ ye _____

Lesson 30

Consonant Digraphs
hn, kn

Name:

 1 Draw a line to match the pictures to the words.

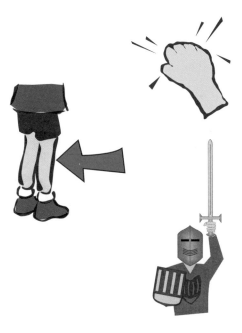

John

knight

knock

knife

knot

knee

2 Use the words from the list to answer the riddles.

Word List					
knit	knights	knee	John	knife	knot

1. You do this to make mittens or socks. What is it?

2. These men wore suits of armor. Who were they?

3. To make this, you need string or a rope. What is it?

Horizons® Phonics & Reading Grade 1 Student Book One

4. This is the part of your leg that bends when you walk. What is it?

_____

5. This is a boy's name. What is it?

_____

6. This used to cut things. What is it?

_____

3 **Draw lines to match the words that rhyme.**

shot	knit
life	knight
right	know
free	knot
row	knee
sit	knife

4 **Write three sentences using at least four of the words from above.**

1. _____

2. _____

3. _____

1. Read each sentence. Circle the words that contain vowel digraphs *oo*, *ea*, *aw*, *au*, or *ei*.

1. The children played eight games at recess.

2. Jim saw the shooting star.

3. Paul likes white bread for sandwiches.

4. We stood and waited for our moms.

5. Jack caught the football and ran to the end zone.

2. Read each sentence. Underline the word that correctly completes the sentence. Write the word on the line.

1. Mary is talking on the _____ .

                          can   phone

2. She _____ that she can go outside.

       catch   doubts

3. She is talking to her _____ .

            trick   nephew

4. His name is _____ .

       name   Phil

3. Circle the consonants in these words, then cross out the consonants that are silent.

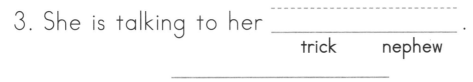

column   solemn   diaphragm

4 Read each sentence. Use the words from the list to complete the sentences.

Word List

| flock | back | check | crack |

1. Jan had to _____ on her little brother.

2. There was a _____ in the clock.

3. There are thirty sheep in the _____.

4. We went _____ to our house.

5 Read the words in the word list. Put the words in the correct categories.

Word List

| right | rough | night | tough |
| high | enough | weigh | laugh |

Silent gh	Digraph gh makes f sound

Rule:

In consonant digraph *mb*, the *b* is silent and the *m* is pronounced, as in *comb* and *limb*.

1 Draw lines to match the pictures to the words.

limb

lamb

climb

bomb

comb

2 Read each sentence. Underline the word that completes the sentence. Write the word on the line.

1. Mike needed to _____ his hair.

        came   comb

2. Jean likes to _____ trees.

        climb   clam

3. The tree _____ broke.

        limb   lane

4. A baby sheep is called a _____ .

        lad   lamb

3 Write a short story using at least three of the words in the word list.

Word List

| limb | lamb | climb | bomb | comb |

4 Draw a picture to go with your story.

Rules:

In consonant blend *sc* if the *sc* comes before *e*, *i*, or *y*, the *c* is silent and the *s* is pronounced, as in *scene* or *science*. If the *sc* comes before *a*, *o*, *u*, or a *consonant*, the *s* is pronounced and the *c* has the hard sound, as in *scared* and *scrape*.

1 Draw lines to match the pictures with the words.

scared

scene

scrape

scent

scrap

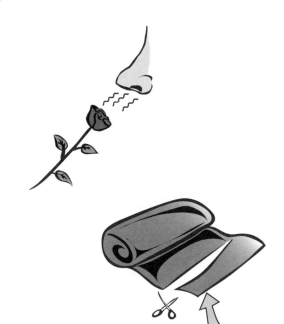

2 Read each sentence. Underline the word that completes the sentence. Write the word on the line.

1. Jane's favorite class is _____ .
   scene   science

2. The _____ of the rose is sweet.
   scent   scrap

3. The sunset was a pretty _____ .
   scrape   scene

4. The bad dream _____ the little girl.
   scared   scored

3 Look at the pictures. Finish the words under each picture with the consonant blend *scr*.

_____ ape   _____ ap   _____ atch   _____ am

4 Use the words from the list to complete the crossword puzzle.

scene   scratch   scrap   scent   scared

ACROSS:
1. The lake was a pretty _____ .
2. A small bit of cloth is a _____ .
3. The rose has a nice _____ .

DOWN:
1. The bad dream _____ the little girl.
2. An itch makes you want to _____ .

Horizons® Phonics & Reading Grade 1 Student Book One

Lesson 33

Review:
Consonant Digraph wh,
Consonant Blends pl, sl, sm

Name: _____

Rule Review:

The consonant digraph *wh* makes the sound you hear in *what* and *when*.

 Look at each picture. Write the name of each picture. Use the words from the list.

Word List

whine	wheel	white	wheat

_____ _____ _____ _____

2 **Read each sentence. Underline the word that completes each sentence. Write the word on the line.**

1. Jan did not know _____ to do.
   where   what

2. The _____ came off her bike.
   wheel   what

3. She did not know _____ it came off.
   why   not

4. Her dad can fix it _____ he gets home.
   when   why

3 Add *sl* to each of the words below, then read the words to your teacher.

___ am ___ ed ___ ip ___ ug

___ id ___ ot ___ it ___ at

4 Look at the pictures. Circle the consonant blend that makes the beginning sound you hear.

sl sm pl   sl sm pl   sl sm pl   sl sm pl

5 Look at the pictures. Finish the words under each picture with the consonant blend *sl* or *sm*.

___ ile ___ ip ___ ell ___ ed

6 Add *pl* to each of the words below, then read the words to your teacher.

___ an ___ op ___ ug ___ ot

Rule:

In consonant digraph *wr*, the *w* is silent and the *r* is pronounced as in *write* and *wrong*.

1. Draw lines to match the pictures with the words.

wrap

wrist

wren

write

wrench

wreck

2. Read each sentence. Underline the word that completes the sentence. Write the word on the line.

1. John did not want to do the _____ thing.
      wrong   what

2. He needed to _____ a letter to his friend.
      when   write

3. The car _____ was bad.
      wreck   when

4. Your _____ is part of your arm.
      where   wrist

5. The _____ had a nest in the tree.
   write   wren

6. Dad fixed my bike with a _____ .
   wrist   wrench

3 **Use the words from the list to complete the sentences.**

Word List				
wren	write	wrench	wreck	wrong

I will _____ a note to Jim. I will tell him about

the _____ that made a nest in the tree. I will

tell him that I had a _____ with my bike. The

tire on the bike was _____ . My dad fixed it

with a _____ .

Rule Review:

In consonant digraph *gn*, the *g* is silent and the *n* is pronounced.
In consonant digraph *hn*, the *h* is silent and the *n* is pronounced as in *John*.
In consonant digraph *kn*, the *k* is silent and the *n* is pronounced as in *knot*.
In consonant digraph *mb*, the *b* is silent and the *m* is pronounced.
The consonant digraph *wh* makes the sound you hear in *what* and *when*.
In consonant digraph *wr*, the *w* is silent and the *r* is pronounced.
Consonant digraph *ch* makes the beginning sound you hear in *chair*. It can also make the *k* sound as in *chorus*.

Write the consonant digraph that completes each word.

| gn | hn | kn | mb | wh | wr | ch |

co _____

si _____

_____ air

_____ ine

_____ orus

_____ ife

_____ ite

Jo _____

2 Read each sentence. Underline the word that completes the sentence. Write the word on the line.

1. The lake was a very pretty _____ .

   star   scene

2. We do not want to do the _____ thing.

   want   wrong

3. The boy's name is _____ .

   John   join

4. The _____ came off my bike.

   where   wheel

5. I like to _____ gifts.

   wrap   write

3 Write a short story using at least three of the words from the list.

Word List

wrap	scene	wreck	comb	when
wrong	wrench	sign	where	which

Lesson 36

Words with x

Name: _____

Rule:

When *x* comes at the end of a word, it usually is pronounced *ks*, as in *box* and *fox*. When *x* comes at the beginning of a word, it often makes the *z* sound as in *xylophone*. Very few English words begin with the letter *x*.

1 Read each sentence. Underline the word that completes the sentence. Write the word on the line.

1. Meg kept her toys in a _____ .
   boy   box

2. Meg's mom can _____ the car.
   box   fix

3. The _____ chased a rabbit.
   fox   fun

4. A _____ comes at the end of a word.
   same   suffix

5. He cuts wood with an _____ .
   all   ax

2 Write the name of each picture.

 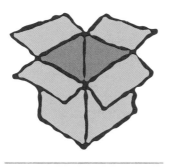  

_____   _____   _____   _____

Read the story. Write the words that complete the story on the lines. Use the words from the list. You will have to use some of the words two times.

Word List

ax	fix	box	fox

A man with an _____ went into the woods. He went

to _____ a _____ of wood to take home.

He saw a _____ run into the _____ to hide

from a dog. The dog did not find the _____ .

4 **Add x to each of the words below, then read the words to your teacher.**

fa____   bo____   es____   fi____   mi____

Ma____   fo____   si____   ta____

Rule:

The beginning consonant blends *pr*, *tr*, *fr*, and *sn* work together to make the sounds you hear in <u>pr</u>ess, <u>tr</u>ip, <u>fr</u>og, and <u>sn</u>ack.

1 Draw lines to match the pictures with the words.

press

track

print

snack

trap

frog

2 Add *sn* to each of the words below, then read the words to your teacher.

_____ ip   _____ iff   _____ ap   _____ ug

3 Look at the pictures. Circle the consonant blend that makes the beginning sound you hear.

pr   tr   fr   pr   tr   fr   pr   tr   fr   pr   tr   fr

_____ oth   _____ og   _____ ank   _____ esh

5 Look at the pictures. Finish the words under each picture by adding the correct consonant blend.

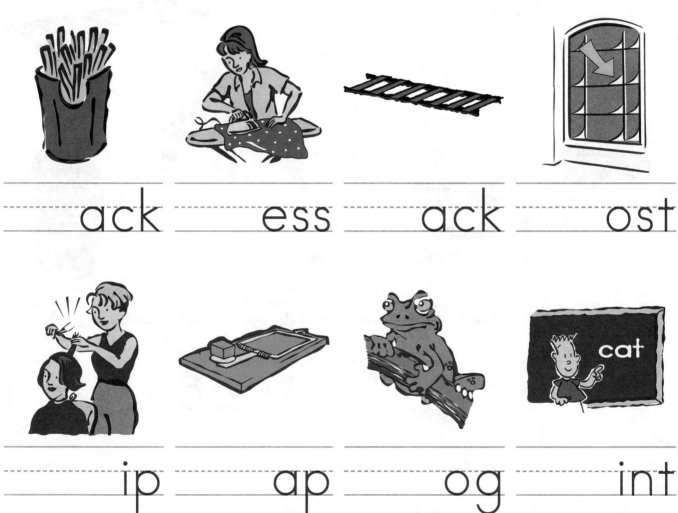

_____ ack   _____ ess   _____ ack   _____ ost

_____ ip   _____ ap   _____ og   _____ int

Rule:

A *contraction* is a word that is made from two words. Two words are put together, and one or more letters are left out. In contractions formed with the word *will*, an apostrophe (') is used in place of the letters that are left out. Examples: *you will = you'll* and *I will = I'll*. In contractions formed with the word *not*, an apostrophe (') is used in place of the letters that are left out. Examples: *cannot = can't* and *could not = couldn't*.

1 Draw lines to match the contractions with the groups of words from which they are made.

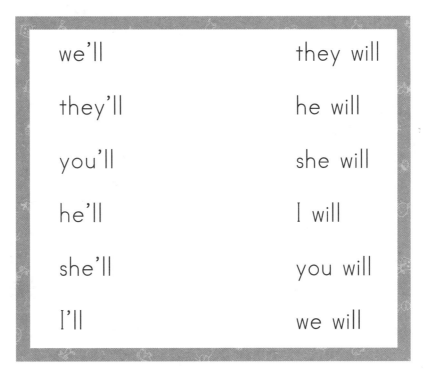

we'll	they will
they'll	he will
you'll	she will
he'll	I will
she'll	you will
I'll	we will

2 Write the correct contraction for each group of words.

I will _____   they will _____

she will _____   you will _____

he will _____   we will _____

3 Draw lines to match the contractions with the groups of words from which they are made.

don't	will not
can't	do not
won't	could not
shouldn't	cannot
wouldn't	was not
didn't	did not
hadn't	had not
couldn't	would not
doesn't	should not
wasn't	does not

4 Read each sentence. Write the correct *contraction* on the line.

1. Jim _____ want to go to the party.
   does not

2. He is afraid that he _____ know anyone.
   will not

3. Jim's mom says that he_____ worry.
   should not

4. He still _____ want to go.
   did not

Rule:

The ending consonant blends *lk*, *lt*, *lf*, and *ft* work together to make the sounds you hear in *sulk*, *wilt*, *self*, and *soft*.

1 Look at the pictures. Circle the consonant blend that makes the ending sound you hear.

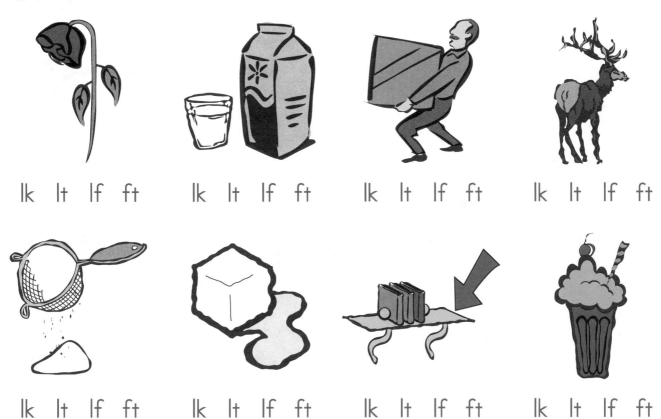

lk lt lf ft   lk lt lf ft   lk lt lf ft   lk lt lf ft

lk lt lf ft   lk lt lf ft   lk lt lf ft   lk lt lf ft

2 Look at the pictures above and add the correct ending consonant blend to each of the words below. Then read the words to your teacher.

wi____   mi____   li____   e____

si____   me____   she____   ma____

3 Draw lines to match the words that rhyme.

shelf	gift
melt	molt
bolt	loft
lift	silk
wilt	self
soft	belt
milk	tilt

4 Read each riddle. Choose the correct word from the list to answer each riddle. Write the word on the line.

Word List

gift	melt	silk	elk	sift	salt

1. Snow will do this in the hot sun. _____

2. Mom does this when she bakes. _____

3. A soft kind of cloth. _____

4. You use this on your food. _____

5. A large animal with antlers. _____

6. You give this to someone. _____

122

Rule Review:

A *contraction* is a word that is made from two words. Two words are put together, and one or more letters are left out. An apostrophe (') is used in place of the letters that are left out.

Read the story. Circle each of the contractions in the story. On the lines below the story write the *two words* for each contraction you circled.

Spot was a little dog. He was white with black spots. He wasn't a mean dog. He liked everyone.

His owner, Mark, went out to play one day. Mark took Spot with him. It was a very nice day. They played fetch with a ball. Mark didn't want to come in when his mom called him. But Mark knew that if he disobeyed his mother, he wouldn't get to play outside the next day. Mark took Spot and went inside.

Spot thought to himself, "We'll go out and play tomorrow. I'll have fun with Mark." And he did!

1. _____

2. _____

3. _____

4. _____

5. _____

2 Read each sentence. Write the correct contraction on the line.

1. You _____ do mean things.
   should not

2. I _____ like that.
   would not

3. We _____ be there.
   will not

4. _____ be your friend.
   I will

3 Write the two words that make up each contraction.

1. won't

_____

2. shouldn't

_____

3. he'll

_____

4. couldn't

_____

5. hadn't

_____

6. we'll

_____

7. they'll

_____

8. I'll

_____

9. wouldn't

_____

10. can't

_____

1 Use the consonant digraphs *sc*, *wh*, or *wr* to complete the words.

1. _____ ench

2. _____ ene

3. _____ ine

4. _____ eat

5. _____ ared

6. _____ eck

2 Read each sentence. Use the words from the list to complete the sentences. Write the correct words on the lines.

Word List			
xylophone	ax	fox	box

1. Jim put his toys in a _____.

2. He saw a _____ in the woods.

3. John likes to play the _____.

4. He chops wood with an _____.

Write the two words that make up each contraction.

1. didn't

_____

----

4. you'll

_____

----

2. aren't

_____

----

5. can't

_____

----

3. wouldn't

_____

----

6. won't

_____

----

4 **Look at the pictures. Circle the consonant blend or digraph that makes the *ending* sound you hear.**

 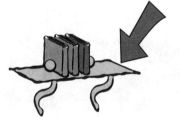  

mb   gn   hn   lk   lt   lf   ck   nd   nt   hn   th   mb

5 **Look at the pictures. Circle the consonant blend or digraph that makes the *beginning* sound you hear.**

pr   tr   fr   sn   scr   sc   wh   wr   ch   kn   sn   fr

Name: _____
_____

Rule:

In contractions formed with the word *have*, the *ha* is removed and replaced with an apostrophe ('). Examples: *I have* = *I've* and *you have* = *you've*.

1 Write the correct contraction for each set of words.

I have _____   they have _____

we have _____   you have _____

2 Read each sentence. Choose a phrase from the list to complete the sentence. Write the *contraction* of that phrase on the line.

Word List			
we have	you have	they have	I have

1. _____ made you laugh.

2. _____ done tricks for you.

3. _____ been running around the ring.

4. We hope _____ liked our show.

We've been planning to have a party. Mom and Dad have been helping us. They've sent out the invitations. I've been planning the games. My sister said, "You've done a good job!"

1. _____

2. _____

3. _____

4. _____

Rule:

In contractions formed with the word *is*, the *i* is removed and replaced with an apostrophe (’). Examples: *he is* = *he's* and *she is* = *she's*.

1 Write the contraction for each set of words.

he is	she is	it is

2 Read each sentence. Use the contractions from the list to complete each sentence.

It's	She's	He's

1. _____ going to wear a dress to school.

2. _____ going to wear his new pants.

3. _____ going to be a good day at school.

3 Write the two words that make up each contraction.

she's   it's   he's

_____   _____   _____

_____   _____   _____

Rule:

In an *r-controlled vowel*, an *r* after the vowel makes the vowel sound different from a short or long sound. Examples: <u>*star*</u>, <u>*shirt*</u>, <u>*term*</u>, <u>*born*</u>, <u>*burn*</u>.

4 Look at the pictures. Finish the words under each picture with the correct r-controlled vowel.

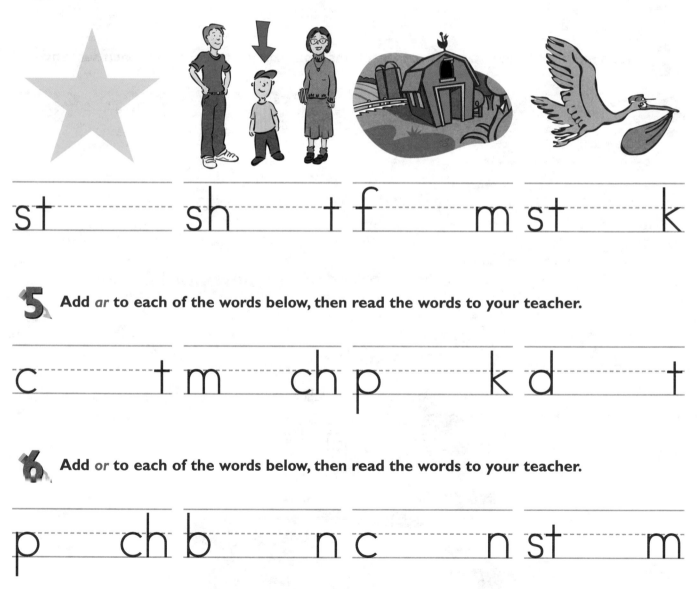

st ____   sh ____ t   f ____ m   st ____ k

5 Add *ar* to each of the words below, then read the words to your teacher.

c ____ t   m ____ ch   p ____ k   d ____ t

6 Add *or* to each of the words below, then read the words to your teacher.

p ____ ch   b ____ n   c ____ n   st ____ m

Rule Review:

A *contraction* is a word that is made from two words. Two words are put together, and one or more letters are left out. An apostrophe (') is used in place of the letters that are left out.

1 Write the two words that make up each contraction.

you've	she's	we've

it's	he's	I've

2 Write a short story using at least three of the contractions from above.

3 **Read each sentence. Use the contractions from the list to complete each sentence. Use each contraction only once.**

Word List

We've	It's	She's	He's	I've

1. _____ having fun with his friend.

2. _____ been here before.

3. _____ done our homework for school.

4. _____ walking her friend home.

5. _____ a rainy day.

Rule:

In contractions formed with the words *am* and *us*, the vowel is removed and replaced with an apostrophe ('). Examples: *I am* = *I'm* and *let us* = *let's*.

1 Draw lines to match the picture with the phrase that describes it.

Let's play.

I'm running.

Let's ride.

I'm eating.

2 Write the two words that make up each contraction.

I'm	let's

3 **Read each sentence. Underline the contraction that correctly completes each sentence. Write the contraction on the line.**

1. My mom knows that _____ going outside.

                                              can't   I'm

2. She said, "_____ go to the park."

                     Let's   You've

3. _____ happy that we get to go.

     You've   I'm

4. _____ play on the swings.

     She's   Let's

Rules:

In contractions formed with the word *are*, the vowel is removed and replaced with an apostrophe (*'*). Examples: *you are* = *you're* and *they are* = *they're*.
Consonant blends *spr* and *spl* are used at the beginning of words and make the sounds you hear in *spring* and *splash*.

1. Draw lines to match the picture with the phrase that describes it.

We're having a party.

They're climbing.

You're my best friend.

They're running.

 2. Write the two words that make up each contraction.

we're	they're	you're

3 Read each sentence. Underline the contraction that correctly completes each sentence. Write the contraction on the line.

1. _____ having a picnic in the park.
   Let's   We're

2. _____ going to come to the picnic.
   They're   They'll

3. _____ going to have a lot of fun in the park.
   I'll   You're

4 Look at the pictures. Finish the words under each picture with the consonant blend *spl* or *spr*.

_____ay   _____ing   _____out   _____ash

5 Add *spl* to each of the words below, then read the words to your teacher.

_____ash   _____it   _____int   _____at

Lesson 46

Review: Contractions
with Am, Are, & Us,
Consonant Blend st

Name: _____

Rule Review:

A *contraction* is a word that is made from two words. Two words are put together, and one or more letters are left out. An apostrophe (') is used in place of the letters that are left out.

Consonant blend *st* can be used at the beginning or end of a word, as in <u>st</u>and and re<u>st</u>.

1 Write three sentences. Use some of the words from the list.

Word List				
I'm	you're	let's	we're	they're

1. _____

_____

_____

2. _____

_____

_____

3. _____

_____

_____

2 Add *st* to each of the words below, then read the words to your teacher.

____ and ____ ep ____ op ____ ick

3 Draw lines to match the picture with the phrase that describes it. Draw a circle around the contraction in each sentence.

They're playing tag.

I'm going to hit a home run.

You're a good dog.

We're going for a drive.

Let's go to the park to play.

4 Add *st* to each of the words below, then read the words to your teacher.

co _____   bla   be   fa

5 Look at the pictures below. Circle the *st* to show whether the *st* sound is at the beginning or at the end of the word.

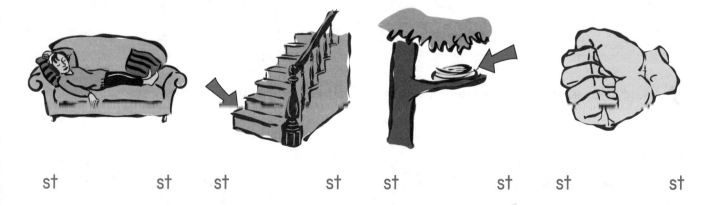

st   st   st   st   st   st   st   st

More Contractions
with Is, Consonant
Blends tw, sw

Name:

Rules:

In contractions formed with the word *is*, the *i* is removed and replaced with an apostrophe ('). **Examples:** *that is* = *that's* and *there* = *there's*.

Consonant blends *tw* and *sw* are used at the beginning of words and make the sounds you hear in *twin* and *swim*.

1. Write the two words that make up each contraction.

he's	they're	she's

that's	it's

2. Read each sentence. Choose a phrase from the list to complete the sentence. Write the *contraction* of that phrase on the line.

Word List

that is	he is	she is	it is

1. _____ going home to his family.

2. _____ his mother.

3. _____ going to be a fun time.

4. _____ his favorite food.

3 Write a sentence to go with each contraction.

1. that's _____

_____

2. there's _____

_____

3. he's _____

_____

4 Add *tw* to each of the words below, then read the words to your teacher.

_____ ist   _____ ins   _____ ig   _____ itch

5 Add *sw* to each of the words below, then read the words to your teacher.

_____ ing   _____ ell   _____ ift   _____ ept

6 Look at the pictures. Circle the consonant blend that makes the beginning sound you hear.

sw   tw   sw   tw   sw   tw   sw   tw

Rule Review:

A *contraction* is a word that is made from two words. Two words are put together, and one or more letters are left out. An apostrophe (') is used in place of the letters that are left out.

Use contractions from the word list to complete the sentences.

Word List

That's

I've

We'll

Don't

1. _____ be sure that we say hello.

2. _____ go too far away.

3. _____ been gone for a long time.

4. _____ all there is.

Draw lines to match the contractions with the words.

can't	will not
it's	cannot
I'm	they have
they've	it is
won't	I am

Use contractions from the list to complete the story.

Word List

didn't	can't	she's	doesn't	aren't

The kitten _____ get down from the tree.

_____ sitting on a high branch.

She _____ want to climb down. They

_____ have any trouble getting the kitten

down. _____ you glad the kitten has such

caring friends?

Horizons® Phonics & Reading Grade 1 Student Book One

Review: Compound Words

Name: _____

Rule Review:

A compound word is a word made from two or more words joined together to make one word. Examples: *backyard*, *runway*, *mailbox*.

1 Draw lines to match the pictures to the words.

backpack

doghouse

raincoat

mailbox

railroad

cupcake

peanut

2 Draw a line to divide each compound word into its two separate words.

myself   baseball

maybe   cupcake

popcorn   seaweed

Use words from the list to finish the story.

Word List

maybe	mailbox	sunshine	raincoat

I went to the _____ to get the mail. I had

to wear my _____ because it was raining.

_____ tomorrow it will be nice and there

will be _____ .

Rule Review:

If a short vowel word ends in a single consonant, usually double the consonant before adding a suffix that begins with a vowel. Examples: *run/running*, *dig/digging*.

1. Write the words, adding the *-ing* suffix at the end of each word.

run _____   pass _____

dig _____   miss _____

hop _____   buzz _____

2. Read each sentence. Underline the word that correctly completes the sentence. Write the word on the line.

1. Jack was _____ the ball to Mary.

   telling   passing

2. She was always _____ it.

   buzzing   missing

3. Jack was _____ to catch the ball.

   running   digging

4. He was _____ Mary with it.

   mailing   tagging

Use the words from the list to complete the crossword puzzle.

getting   tagging   netting   digging

ACROSS:
1. The dog is _____ in the dirt.
3. John was _____ his friend with the ball.
4. Jane was _____ a butterfly.

DOWN:
2. Dave is _____ a surprise for his birthday.

1 Write the two words that make up each contraction

1. didn't

2. aren't

3. I'll

4. you'll

5. I've

6. let's

7. I'm

8. we've

9. it's

10. you're

11. we're

12. won't

2 Look at the pictures. Circle the consonant blend that makes the beginning sound you hear.

st   tw   sw   st   tw   sw   st   tw   sw   st   tw   sw

3 Look at the pictures. Circle the consonant blend that makes the beginning sound you hear.

spl   spr   spl   spr   spl   spr   spl   spr

4 Look at the pictures. Finish the words under each picture with correct consonant blend.

_____ ne   _____ ick   _____ itch   _____ ig

5 Write the words, adding the *-ing* suffix at the end of each word.

run _____   pass _____

dig _____   miss _____

hop   buzz

6 Draw a line to divide each compound word into its two separate words.

backpack   cupcake   peanut   doghouse

Name: _____

Rule:

A suffix is an ending that is added to a base word. Many words do not have to have their spelling changed before the suffix is added. Examples: *jump/jumped*, *lock/locked*.

1. Add the suffix *-ed* to each base word. Write the new word on the line.

fix _____   clean _____

pass _____   paint _____

want _____   play _____

mail _____   help _____

2. Use words from the list to complete the sentences.

Word List

cheered	played	jumped	wished	wanted

1. The boys _____ soccer.

2. They _____ to win the game.

3. Each boy _____ that he could make a goal.

4. John _____ up and down when he scored.

5. The fans _____ for him.

Read the story. Underline all of the words containing the suffix -ed. Write the words on the lines.

Dad and I fished in the lake. The fish jumped in and out of the water. Dad looked at his pole. He had hooked a fish! Dad pulled the fish out of the lake. Then Dad helped me bait my hook, and we both waited for a fish to bite.

1. _____

2. _____

3. _____

4. _____

5. _____

6. _____

7. _____

Review: Suffixes -s & -es,
R-Controlled Vowels er, ir, ur **Name:** _____

Rule:

A suffix is an ending that is added to a base word. Many words do not have to have their spelling changed before the suffix is added, as in *like/likes*. If a word ends in *ss*, *ch*, *sh*, or *x*, you usually add *es* to make the word plural, as in *church/churches*.

1 Make a new word by adding the suffixes *-s* or *-es*. Write the words on the lines.

jump _____   church _____

brush _____   need _____

touch _____   plan _____

play _____   walk _____

2 Read each word. Circle the base word. Remember, a base word is a word without a prefix or a suffix.

likes	plays	touches	hops
jumps	runs	brushes	walks

3 Read each sentence. Use a word from the list above to complete the sentence.

1. Sarah _____ to school.

2. She _____ with her friends after school.

3. She _____ to play tag.

Rule:

In an *r-controlled vowel*, an *r* after the vowel makes the vowel sound different from a short or long sound. Examples: st*ar*, sh*ir*t, t*er*m, b*or*n, b*ur*n.

4 Add *er* to each of the words below, then read the words to your teacher.

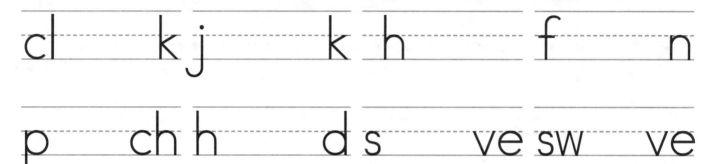

cl   kj   k   h   f   n

p   ch h   d s   ve sw   ve

5 Add *ir* to each of the words below, then read the words to your teacher.

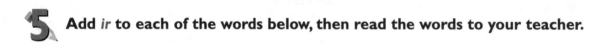
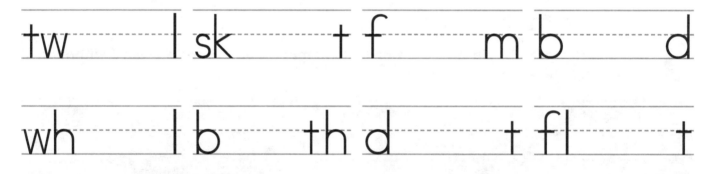

tw   l sk   t f   m b   d

wh   l b   th d   t fl   t

6 Add *ur* to each of the words below, then read the words to your teacher.

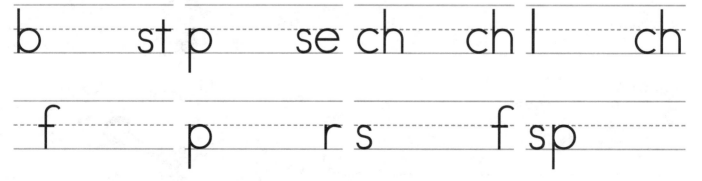

b   st p   se ch   ch l   ch

f   p   r s   f sp

Lesson 53

Review:
Suffix -ful

Name: _____

Rule:

When adding the suffix *-ful* to a base word, the spelling of the base word usually does not change. Examples: *pain/painful*, *play/playful*, *care/careful*.

1 Make a new word by adding the suffix *-ful*. Write the words on the lines.

help _____

pain _____

hope _____

care _____

joy _____

2 Read each word. Circle the base words.

careful	useful	restful	colorful
helpful	harmful	playful	fearful

3 Write a short story. Use at least three of the words from the list above.

_____

_____

_____

_____

_____

Read each sentence. Use a word from the list to complete the sentence.

1. Jason's new puppy was very _____ .

2. The map was _____ when we got lost.

3. The butterfly was very _____ .

4. Chad got a _____ scrape on his knee.

5. "Be _____ when you cross
   the street," said Mom.

Rule:

When adding the suffixes *-ness* or *-less* to a base word, the spelling of the base word usually does not change. Examples: *sad/sadness, hope/hopeless.*

1 Read each word. Add the suffixes *-ness* or *-less* to make new words. Write the words on the lines.

-ness	-less
dark	help
loud	care
sharp	fear
soft	use

2 Match the base word in the first column with the new word in the second column. Write the letter of the correct word on the line.

1. _____ sleeve   a. kindness

2. _____ care   b. goodness

3. _____ sad   c. careless

4. _____ good   d. sadness

5. _____ kind   e. sleeveless

3 **Use words from the list to complete the sentences.**

Word List

useless	careless	helpless	kindness	darkness

1. He needed a light to see in the _____ .

2. The broken glass was _____ .

3. We should show _____ to other people.

4. If you are _____ when you ride your bike, you may get hurt.

5. The kitten in the tree was _____ . It could not get down by itself.

Rule:

When adding the suffix *-ly* to a base word, the spelling of the base word usually does not change. Examples: *quick/quickly*, *brave/bravely*.

1 Read each word. Add the suffix *-ly* to make new words. Write the words on the lines.

glad _____   safe _____

soft _____   slow _____

love _____

2 Read each sentence. Use the new words from above to complete the sentences. Write the words on the lines.

1. Jack _____ got out of bed. He was tired and didn't move very fast.

2. The necklace is very _____.

3. The kitten purred _____. He could hardly be heard.

4. The boy wanted to cross the street _____, so he looked both ways first.

3. The boy _____ helped his mom.

3 Read the words in the list. Write each word next to its definition.

> ## Word List
>
> slowly   safely   gladly   bravely

1. In a safe way: _____

2. In a way that is glad: _____

3. In a brave way: _____

4. In way that is slow: _____

4 Draw a line to match the base words with the words that have the *-ly* suffix added.

brave	suddenly
safe	lonely
sudden	gladly
lone	safely
glad	bravely

Horizons® Phonics & Reading Grade 1 Student Book One

Review:
Suffixes -y, -en, -able

Name:

Rule:

When a word ends in a single or a double consonant, the spelling does not usually need to be changed when adding the suffixes -y, -en, or -able. Examples: *speed/speedy, soft/soften, wear/wearable.*

1 Add the suffix -y to make new words.

trick _____

curl _____

thirst _____

wind _____

speed _____

2 Add the suffix -en to make new words.

soft _____

sharp _____

wood _____

dark _____

fright _____

3 Add the suffix -able to make new words.

suit _____

sink _____

wear _____

wash _____

break _____

Read each sentence. Use the words in the list to complete the sentences. Write the words on the lines.

Word List

speedy	suitable	sharpen	curly	breakable

1. His clothes were not _____ for cold weather.

2. The glass was very _____.

3. The race car was very _____.

4. The boy had _____ red hair.

5. Dad had to _____ the ax before he could chop wood.

Read each word. Circle the base words.

speedy	curly	wooden	frighten
suitable	breakable	soften	speedy
sharpen	tricky	darken	washable

Lesson 57

Review:
Suffix -er

Name: _____

Rule:

The suffix *-er* can be used to compare two things. Examples: *near/nearer, long/longer.*

1 **Read each word. Add the suffix *-er* to make new words. Write the new words on the lines.**

fast _____   deep _____

dark _____   light _____

soft _____   smart _____

2 **Read each word. Draw a picture below each word to show its meaning.**

faster	longer	taller

3 Read each sentence. Use the words from the list to complete each sentence. Write the words on the lines.

Word List

deeper	taller	softer	faster

1. Susan runs _____ than Mary.

2. The water is _____ at the other end of the pool.

3. My cat's fur was _____ after I brushed it.

4. He is _____ than his brother.

Name: _____

Rule:

When a word ends in y after a consonant, change the y to *i* before adding -er to the end.
Examples: *pretty/prettier* and *busy/busier*.

1 Read each word. Make a new word by adding the suffix *-er* to the base word. Remember to change the y to an *i* before you add the *-er* at the end of the word.

busy _____   happy _____

sunny _____   silly _____

funny _____   early _____

2 Read each sentence. Choose the correct word to complete the sentence. Then write the word on the line.

1. Joan was much _____ after school started.
   busyer   busier

2. Today is _____ than it was yesterday.
   sunnier   sunnyer

3. My dog is _____ than my cat is.
   sillyest   sillier

4. We had to get up _____ today.
   earliest   earlier

Draw a line to match the base words with the words that have the -er suffix added.

happy	earlier
sunny	sillier
windy	busier
silly	happier
early	windier
busy	sunnier

 Here are some long ā words that rhyme. Read the words in each list.

bake	make	fake	Jake
name	came	dame	fame
rate	Kate	slate	state
slave	wave	pave	Dave
male	sale	gale	vale

 Find and circle ten long ā words.

Word List

ape	Dan	brave	flake	lass
tan	race	nap	snake	drape
tape	pane	jam	sane	paint

Name: _____

Rule:

The suffix *-est* is used to compare more than two things. Examples: *tall/tallest*, *short/shortest*.

1. Read each word. Make a new word by adding the suffix *-est* to the base word. Write the new words on the lines.

near _____   soft _____

fast _____   dark _____

deep _____   long _____

2. Read each word. Draw a picture below each word to show its meaning.

fastest	longest	tallest

3 Read each sentence. Complete the sentences by adding *-est* to the correct base words from the list. Write the new words on the lines.

Word List

deep	tall	fast	hard	soft

1. Her cat has the _____ fur.

2. Nora is the _____ runner in her class.

3. Jim is the _____ boy on his team.

4. Math is my _____ class.

5. The lake is _____ in the middle.

4 Read the words. Draw a *square* around all the words that have the long ī sound.

bike	stitch	swing	switch	trike
shin	glide	pike	hive	slime
site	prim	smile	pitch	pink
trip	pride	thin	spring	shine

5 Find and circle ten long ō words.

mope	phone	scope	drop	pole
mop	smoke	stock	drove	pool
hope	smock	scroll	joke	molt

Horizons® Phonics & Reading Grade 1 Student Book One

Adding Suffix -est to
Words Ending in y,
Review R-Controlled Vowels

Name: _____

Rule:

When a word ends in **y** after a consonant, change the **y** to **i** before adding **-est** to the end.
Examples: *pretty/prettiest* and *lonely/loneliest*.

1. Read each word. Make new words by adding the suffix **-est** to the end of each word.
Remember to change the **y** to **i** before you add **-est**.

silly _____   early _____

happy _____   sunny _____

funny _____   windy _____

2. Complete the sentences by adding **-est** to the base word. Remember to change the **y**
to an **i** before adding **-est** to the end. Write the new words on the lines

1. Today is the _____ day of my life!
   happy

2. March is the _____ month of the year.
   windy

3. The white bunny has the _____ fur.
   fluffy

4. They are the _____ boys I have
   silly
   ever known!

Rule Review:

In an *r-controlled vowel*, an *r* after the vowel makes the vowel sound different from a short or long sound. Examples: *sta**r***, *sh**ir**t*, *t**er**m*, *b**or**n*, *b**ur**n*.

3 Choose the correct r-controlled vowel for the sound you hear in the pictures.

ar er ir or ur   ar er ir or ur   ar er ir or ur   ar er ir or ur

ar er ir or ur   ar er ir or ur   ar er ir or ur   ar er ir or ur

4 Look at the pictures. Finish the words under each picture with the correct r-controlled vowel sound.

p ___ se   h ___ se   c ___ t   s ___ ve

Horizons® Phonics & Reading Grade 1 Student Book One

 Read each of the words. Write the correct *base words* on the lines.

jumped	_____	helpless	_____
showed	_____	hopeful	_____
fluffiest	_____	harden	_____
prettier	_____	soften	_____
sunniest	_____	smaller	_____
happier	_____	dresses	_____
tallest	_____	churches	_____
careful	_____	silliest	_____

2 **Choose the correct r-controlled vowel for the sound you hear in the pictures.**

ar er ir or ur   ar er ir or ur   ar er ir or ur   ar er ir or ur

3 **Read each sentence. Complete each sentence by adding the correct suffix to the base word. Write the new words on the lines.**

1. Jack was _____ that his team would win.
   hope

2. Joan is a very _____ girl.
   cheer

3. There are two _____ on my street.
   church

4. Be sure that you pet the cat _____ .
   soft

5. This has been the _____ day this week.
   sunny

6. I am _____ than my brother.
   tall

4 **Look at the pictures. Finish the words under each picture with the correct r-controlled vowel sound.**

c _ _ n   s _ _ ve   b _ _ n   sh _ _ t

Name: _____

Rule Review:

The suffix **-er** is used to compare two things.
The suffix **-est** is used to compare more than two things.
When a word ends in **y** after a consonant, change the **y** to **i** before adding the suffix **-er**.
When a word ends in **y** after a consonant, change the **y** to **i** before adding the suffix **-est**.

1 Add **-er** or **-est** to each base word to make a new word. Write the word on the line.

1. He is the _____ boy in his class.
   tall

2. She thinks that her red dress is _____ than
   her blue one.   pretty

3. My dog is the _____ dog on my street.
                  friendly

4. We stayed at Bill's house _____ today
   than we did yesterday.   long

5. An ant is _____ than a bird.
              small

2 Find and circle ten words that have the sound of long ū.

club	clue	truck	rule	suit
cube	fruit	mule	tuba	flute
clutch	glue	mull	tub	blue

3 Use the words from the list to complete the crossword puzzle.

earlier   windiest   silliest   sunnier

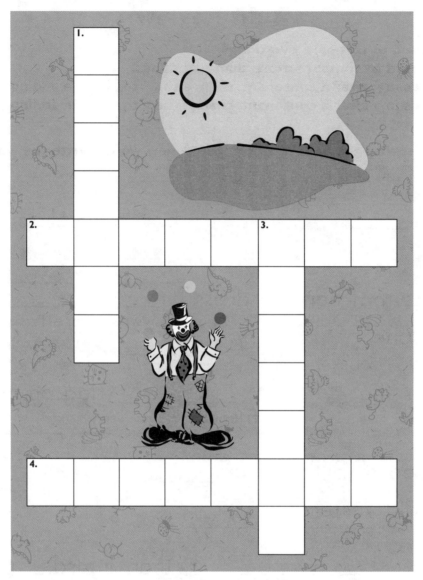

ACROSS:
2. That clown is the _____ one I have ever seen.
4. Today is the _____ day we've had all week.

DOWN:
1. Today is _____ than yesterday.
3. We had to wake up _____ today.

4 Here are some long $\bar{u}$ words that rhyme. Read the words in each list.

blue	glue	clue	true
cube	tube	rude	dude
due	cue	Sue	hue

Lesson 62

Adding Suffix -es to
Words Ending in y,
Review Long Vowel ē

Name: _____

Rule:

When a word ends in **y** after a consonant, usually change the **y** to an **i** before adding *-es*.
Examples: *bunny/bunnies, city/cities*.

1 Read each base word. Add the suffix *-es* to each word to make a new word. Remember to change the **y** to an **i** before you add *-es* to the end. Write the word on the line.

pony _____   lily _____

bunny _____   cherry _____

city _____   candy _____

story _____   penny _____

2 Read each word. Circle the word that goes with the picture.

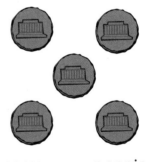

bunnies   bunny   lily   lilies   penny   pennies

3 Find and circle ten long ē words.

teeth	tree	bee	sleep	kelp
tent	feet	spell	elk	elephant
seal	meat	eagle	team	sweep

4 Use the words from the list to write a short story.

Word List			
pony	cherry	penny	city
lily	candy	bunny	story

_____

- -

_____

- -

_____

- -

_____

- -

_____

- -

_____

5 Here are some long ē words that rhyme. Read the words in each list.

treat	meat	seat	beat
sweet	fleet	feet	street
weep	creep	sweep	peep
wheel	feel	reel	steel
cream	beam	steam	dream

Horizons® Phonics & Reading Grade 1 Student Book One

Review:
Suffixes -es, -er,
-est in Words Ending in y

Name: _____

Rule Review:

When a word ends in **y** after a consonant, change the **y** to **i** before adding the suffix **-es**.
When a word ends in **y** after a consonant, change the **y** to **i** before adding the suffix **-er**.
When a word ends in **y** after a consonant, change the **y** to **i** before adding the suffix **-est**.

Read each sentence. Use words from the list to complete each sentence.

Word List

pennies   stories   parties   daisies   candies

1. We planted _____ in our yard.

2. I ate three _____ for a snack.

3. One dollar is worth 100 _____ .

4. I went to two birthday _____ in one day!

5. Mom read two _____ to me before bedtime.

Read each word. Add -es, -er, or -est to each base word to make a new word. Two of the words will have both -er and -est added to them.

pony   _____

baby   _____

happy   _____

cherry   _____

family   _____

funny   _____

3 **Find the words in the word search. The words will be going across or up and down.**

parties	stories	ponies	candies
happier	earliest	funnier	fluffiest

```
s  h  a  p  p  i  e  r  f
t  e  c  a  p  p  l  e  l
o  l  a  r  a  o  f  l  u
r  l  n  t  n  n  o  o  f
i  o  d  i  e  i  e  s  f
e  v  i  e  s  e  a  f  i
s  l  e  s  o  s  r  m  e
b  e  s  t  t  a  r  u  s
e  a  r  l  i  e  s  t  t
o  f  u  n  n  i  e  r  e
```

Write a story.

Your story can be about anything that you would like to write about. Before you write your story, talk to your teacher about ideas. Try to come up with three different things to write about. Then choose from your list of three.

After you have written your story, read it with your teacher or your writing partner. Have your teacher check your story. Make sure that you have spelled all the words correctly and that you have used capital letters where they are needed (names of people and places). Then you may write your final copy with no mistakes.

Write your first copy on a separate sheet of paper. Write your final copy on the lines on the back of this page.

Name: _____

Rule:

A *contraction* is a word that is made from two words. Two words are put together, and one or more letters are left out. An apostrophe (') is used in place of the letters that are left out.

1 Read each sentence. Write the correct *contraction* on the line.

1. _____ having a lot of fun.
   We are

2. _____ brought games with them.
   They have

3. Joan _____ feeling well.
   is not

4. _____ making popcorn.
   I am

5. _____ drinking lemonade.
   He is

2 Draw lines to match the contractions with the words.

they're   I have

I've   should have

won't   they are

should've   will not

3 **Read the story. Underline the contractions in the story. On the lines below the story, write the *two words* that make up each contraction.**

Joan says that she won't be going to the zoo with us tomorrow. She has a bad cold. Her mom says that she's too sick to go anywhere. I've had colds before, and they aren't any fun. We'll stop by her house on the way home and try to cheer her up. I'll be sure that I don't get too close to her!

1. _____   5. _____

2. _____   6. _____

3. _____   7. _____

4. _____

Horizons® Phonics & Reading Grade 1 Student Book One

Lesson

66

Review:
Vowel Pairs ai & ay

Name: _____

Rule:

A vowel pair is two vowels that come together to make one long vowel sound. The first vowel is long, and the second vowel is silent. Examples: *ai/paint* and *ay/may*.

✎ Look at each picture. Below each picture, write the word that goes with it. Use the words from the list.

Word List

pray	drain	play	train	spray	wait

_____

_____

_____

_____

_____

_____

2 Read each sentence. Use a word from the list to complete each sentence. Write the word on the line.

Word List

clay   today   painted   train   play

1. _____ in art class we used _____ .

2. I made a toy _____ .

3. After our projects dried, we _____ them.

4. In my art class, work seems more like _____ .

Review:
Vowel Pairs ee & ea

Name:

Rule:

A vowel pair is two vowels that come together to make one long vowel sound. The first vowel is long, and the second vowel is silent. Examples: *ee/wheel* and *ea/teach*.

Read each word. Circle the word that goes with the picture. Write the word on the lines.

seem   seat

spell   wheel

teach   tree

read   sleep

running   sleeping

wheel   wheat

2 Read each sentence. Use a word from the list to complete each sentence. Write the word on the line.

Word List					
sleeping	wheel	eat	teaching	seat	reading

1. He is _____ a good book.

2. By 8:00, I'm _____.

3. My bike needs a new _____.

4. My mom is _____ me to cook.

5. It was time to _____, so I took my _____ at the table.

Lesson 68

Name: _____

Rule:

A vowel pair is two vowels that come together to make one long vowel sound. The first vowel is long, and the second vowel is silent. Examples: *ie*/*pie* and *oe*/*toe*.

1 Read each sentence. Circle the word that completes the sentence correctly. Write the word on the line.

1. _____ was playing outside.

   Day   Joe   Jot

2. He saw a _____ in the woods.

   doe   dawn   draw

3. It stopped to _____ down in the grass.

   jump   lie   stop

4. Joe stopped to _____ his shoe.

   tie   two   ton

2 Write the name for each picture on the lines below it. Use the words from the list.

Word List

| tie | pie | hoe | doe |

_____   _____   _____   _____

Read the story. Circle all the words that have the vowel pairs *ie*, *ea*, and *oe* in them. Use the words from the story to answer the questions after the story.

Sarah and her mom made a pie. They made peach pie. Sarah liked peach pie best. Sarah's brother Joe helped as much as he could. He was only three years old.

When the pie was cool, each of them had a slice. It was very good!

Sarah said, "Let's make cherry pie next time."

Mom said, "That's a good idea, Sarah!"

1. What did Sarah and her mom make?

----

2. Who helped Sarah and her mom make the pie?

----

3. What kind of pie did they make?

✎ **Write a friendly letter.**

A friendly letter contains five parts:

1. Heading
2. Greeting
3. Body
4. Closing
5. Signature

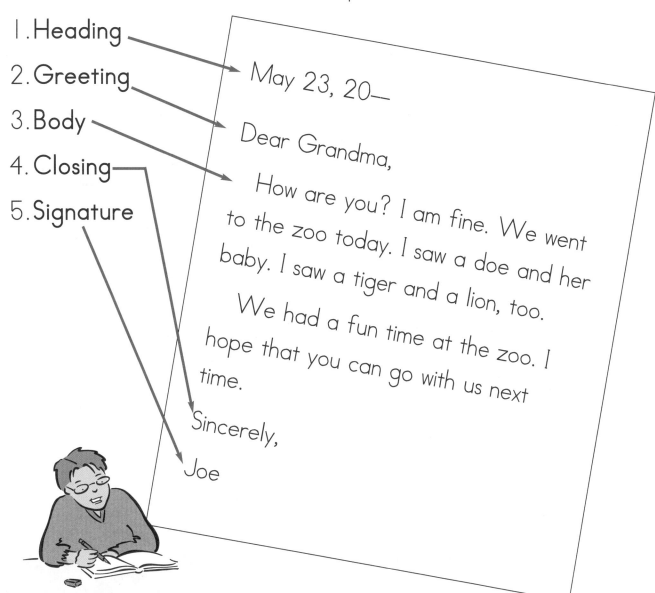

May 23, 20—

Dear Grandma,

How are you? I am fine. We went to the zoo today. I saw a doe and her baby. I saw a tiger and a lion, too.

We had a fun time at the zoo. I hope that you can go with us next time.

Sincerely,

Joe

Write a friendly letter to someone. When you are finished with your letter, read it to your teacher. Have your teacher check your work. Write your first copy on a piece of paper. Write your final copy on the lines on the back of this page.

Name: _____

Rule:

Vowel digraphs are two vowels put together in a word that make a long or short sound or have a special sound all their own. The vowel digraph oo can stand for the vowel sound heard in *book* or in *pool*.

1 Read each sentence. Choose the word that will complete each sentence correctly. Write the word on the lines.

1. The air is very _____ today.
   new   cool

2. Joe is reading a very thick _____.
   look   book

3. We will ride the bus to _____.
   tool   school

4. Dad uses an ax to chop _____.
   stood   wood

5. She shares a _____ with her sister.
   took   room

2 Draw lines to match the words that rhyme.

book	pool
wood	took
loom	stood
tool	room

Draw lines to match the pictures with the words.

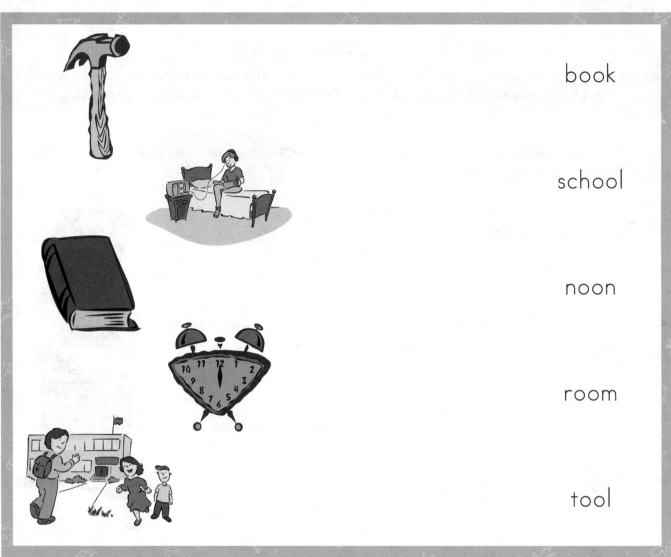

book

school

noon

room

tool

Write a sentence, using at least three of the words shown above.

1 **Read each sentence. Add the correct suffix to the base word and make a new word to complete the sentence. Write the new word on the lines.**

1. They have the _____ yard on our street.
   pretty

2. He is the _____ boy in his class.
   small

3. Joan's hair is _____ than Ruth's hair.
   curly

4. New York and Boston are two _____ .
   city

5. Mom read two _____ to me last night.
   story

2 **Write the two words that make up eacn contraction.**

don't	_____	we'll	_____
can't	_____	he's	_____
won't	_____	let's	_____
should've	_____	I'm	_____

3 Use the words from the list to answer the riddles.

Word List

| train | tie | toe | wheels | paint | play |

1. You do this to shoelaces.

_____

2. This is something on your foot.

_____

3. This makes a wall a new color.

_____

4. You do this at recess.

_____

5. This runs on tracks.

_____

6. Cars need these to go.

_____

Rule:

Vowel digraphs are two vowels put together in a word that make a long or short sound or have a special sound all their own. The vowel digraph *ea* can stand for the short *ĕ* sound heard in *head* or in *bread*.

1 Read each sentence. Choose the correct word to complete the sentence. Then write the word on the line.

1. The bird ate the _____ on the sidewalk.

   dread   bread

2. He ran _____ of me.

   ahead   dead

3. She is wearing a _____ coat today.

   heavy   lead

4. I will _____ butter on my bread.

   spread   tread

5. He has a hat on his _____.

   lead   head

2 Draw lines to match the pictures with the words.

bread

sweater

feather

head

Read the story. Use the words from the list to complete the story.

Word List

bread	sweater	head	breakfast

When Jan woke up, it was cold outside. She knew that she

would have to wear a heavy _____ that day.

She went to get some _____ .

Her mom got her a slice of _____ to make

some toast. After she ate and got dressed, Jan put a hat

on her _____ so that she would be warm.

Horizons® Phonics & Reading Grade 1 Student Book One

Rule:

Vowel digraphs are two vowels put together in a word that make a long or short sound or have a special sound all their own. The vowel digraphs *au* and *aw* stand for the sounds heard in *saw* and in *auto*.

1. Read each sentence. Use the words from the list to complete each sentence.

1. _____ is usually a hot month.

2. My brother mows the _____ .

3. My friend's name is _____ .

4. I like to drink with a _____ .

5. When I am tired, I _____ .

6. The man had to _____ the junk away.

Word List

haul

lawn

August

straw

Paula

yawn

2. Draw lines to match the words with the same vowel sounds.

leaf	yawn
cook	book
head	Paul
lawn	bread
haul	read

Read the story. Use the words from the list to complete the story.

Word List

yawn	drawing	lawn	August	haul

Paul didn't want to mow the _____ . It was

_____

_____ , so it was hot outside. Paul's dad

also wanted him to _____ some trash. Paul

wanted to be inside _____ pictures.

Paul gave a big _____ and went outside

to do as his dad had told him.

Rule:

Vowel digraphs are two vowels put together in a word that make a long or short sound or have a special sound all their own. The vowel digraph *ei* makes the long ā sound you hear in *eight*. The vowel digraph *ew* makes the sound you hear in *new*.

1 Draw lines to match the pictures with the words.

reindeer

stew

weight

flew

sleigh

eight

2 Read each sentence. Underline the word that completes each sentence. Write the word on the line.

1. Mary is _____ years old.

   eat   eight

2. She has a _____ tooth.

   new   flew

3. John can lift a lot of _____ .

   weight   want

4. _____ your food well.

   stew   chew

Use the words from the list to complete the crossword puzzle.

new

eight

sleigh

weight

reindeer

ACROSS:

2. Animals that live in cold places

5. Jim can lift a lot of ____ .

DOWN:

1. Opposite of old

3. Comes after the number seven

4. Like a large sled

Read the "silly sentences." Use the words from the list to complete the sentences.

Word List

| freight | reindeer | weights | sleighs | eight | seven |

Wouldn't it be silly if _____ rode in

_____ ?

Wouldn't it be silly if _____ came after _____ ?

Wouldn't it be silly if a baby could lift _____ ?

Wouldn't it be silly if _____ trains had faces?

Vowel Diphthongs
ou & ow

Name:

Rule:

A vowel diphthong is two vowels that blend together to make one sound. The diphthongs *ow* **and** *ou* **make the sounds you hear in** *owl* **and** *south.*

1 Draw lines to match the pictures with the words.

mouth

crown

mouse

cloud

owl

down

cow

brown

2 Use some of the words from above to answer the riddles. Write the words on the lines.

1. This is a very wise bird.

2. This is what a king has on his head.

3. This is the opposite of **up.**

4. This is an animal that gives milk.

5. It is white and fluffy.

Use the words from the list to write a story about the picture.

Word List

crown   brown   mouse   house   owl   cloud   cow

Rule:

The vowel diphthong *ow* can make two sounds: *ow* as in *cow* or *ow* as in *snow*.

1 Read the words in the list. Write each word in the correct box.

Word List

drown	owl	town	below
brown	low	flow	show

ow as in cow	ow as in snow

2 Look at the pictures. Finish the words under each picture with the sound of *ow* as in *show*.

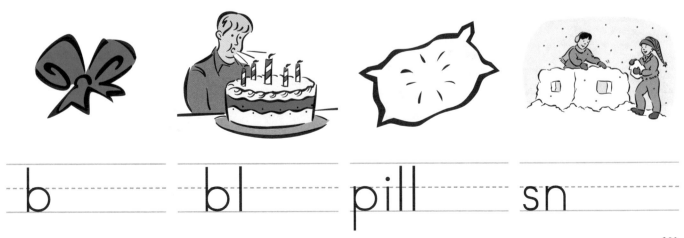

b_____   bl_____   pill_____   sn_____

Read each sentence. Use the words from the list to complete the sentences.

Word List

crown	pillow	snowman	owl

1. The _____ sat in the tree.

2. The king wore a _____ on his head.

3. I sleep on a soft _____.

4. We made a _____ in front of our house.

4. **Read each word in the list. On the lines below, write the *ow* words that have the long ō sound.**

Word List

pillow	now	below	crown
show	clown	flow	snow

1. _____

2. _____

3. _____

4. _____

5. _____

Rule:

A vowel diphthong is two vowels that blend together to make one sound. The diphthongs *oi* and *oy* make the sounds you hear in *coin* and *boy*.

1. Draw lines to match the pictures with the words.

toys

soil

boil

boy

coin

2. Read each sentence. Use the words from above to complete the sentences. Write the word on the line.

1. When the water gets hot, it will _____ .

2. John found a _____ on the floor.

3. We will put away our _____ .

4. John is a good name for a _____ .

5. Plant the seeds in the _____ .

Read the story and answer the questions.

Roy is a boy who likes to collect coins. He has a lot of coins from many different places.

Some of Roy's friends think that his coins are toys, but Roy lets them know that his coins are not toys at all.

1. What does Roy like to collect? _____

2. What do Roy's friends think his coins are? _____

3. Does Roy have a lot of coins? _____

4. Do all the coins come from just one place? _____

Lesson
77

Review:
Vowel Diphthongs
ou & ow

Name: _____

Rule Review:

A vowel diphthong is two vowels that blend together to make one sound. Examples: *ou/south*, *ow/owl*, and *ow/bowl*.

1 Read the questions and answer *yes* or *no*.

1. Do you live in a house? _____

2. Are you a mouse? _____

3. Do you like clowns? _____

4. Is a circle round? _____

5. Do you own a toy? _____

2 Use the words from the list to answer the riddles.

Word List			
bounce	flowers	mouse	round

1. What a ball can do _____

2. The shape of a circle _____

3. A small animal that might like cheese _____

4. Pretty plants we like to pick _____

Horizons® Phonics & Reading Grade 1 Student Book One

205

3 Read each word. Write the words that have the long ō sound.

Word List

flow	count	bounce	show	mouse	snow

_____ _____ _____

- - - - - - - - - - - - - - - - - - - - - - - - - - - - - - - - - - - - - - -

_____ _____ _____

4 Look at the pictures. Complete the words by adding *ou* or *ow*.

sn _____   fl _____ er   m _____ se   b l _____

Rule Review:

A *vowel digraph* has two vowels put together that can make a long or a short sound, or can make a special sound all their own. The vowel digraph *ew* makes the sound you hear in *new*.

 Use the words from the list to complete the crossword puzzle.

drew   few   new   flew   dew   knew

ACROSS:
1. The class _____ the answer.
3. Sarah _____ a picture of her house.
4. A bird ____ by.

DOWN:
2. Jane has a _____ bike.
3. The grass was wet with _____ .
4. The opposite of *many* is _____ .

Write a short story, using words from the list.

Word List

drew	knew	new	crew	threw
blew	flew	grew	jewel	stew

_____

- -

_____

_____

_____

- -

_____

_____

_____

- -

_____

Draw a picture to go with your story.

Horizons® Phonics & Reading Grade 1 Student Book One

Rule Review:

A vowel diphthong is two vowels that blend together to make one sound. The diphthongs *oi* and *oy* make the sounds you hear in *coin* and *boy*. The diphthongs *ou* and *ow* make the sounds you hear in *south* and *owl*. The vowel diphthong *ow* can also make the long ō sound that you hear in *bowl* and *snow*.

Read each sentence. Underline the word that completes each sentence. Write the word on the line.

1. The pan will _____ soon.
   foil   boil

2. We all got in the car and went to _____ .
   town   south

3. A foot of _____ fell last night.
   snow   go

4. Mike is a _____ in my class.
   toy   boy

5. I want to _____ the Girl Scouts.
   toil   join

6. Jane's eyes are _____ .
   brand   brown

Look at the pictures. Circle the correct vowel diphthong.

ow   oy   ou   ow   oy   ou   ow   oy   ou   ow   oy   ou

ow   oy   ou   ow   oy   ou   ow   oy   ou   ow   oy   ou

ow   oy   ou   ow   oy   ou   ow   oy   ou   ow   oy   ou

1 Draw lines to match the pictures with the words.

bread

snowman

cow

coin

joy

stew

seat

eight

2 Read each sentence. Use some of the words from above to complete the sentences. Write the word on the line.

1. We had _____ and _____ for lunch.

2. A _____ gives us milk.

3. Please sit in your _____ .

4. I am _____ years old today.

5. When it snows, we can make a _____ .

3 Write three sentences using words from the list.

Word List

bread	cow	joy	seat
snowman	coin	stew	eight

1. _____

_____

_____

_____

2. _____

_____

_____

_____

3. _____

_____

_____